GW00683408

AIRFIX
magazine guide 22

Russian Tanks of World War 2

John Milsom and
Steve Zaloga

Patrick Stephens Ltd
in association with Airfix Products Ltd

First published — 1977

ISBN 0 85059 250 X

Cover design by Tim McPhee

Text set in 8 on 9pt Univers Medium by Stevenage Printing Limited, Stevenage.
Printed in Great Britain on Fineblade Cartridge 90 gsm and bound by the Garden City Press, Letchworth, Herts.
Published by Patrick Stephens Limited, Bar Hill, Cambridge, CB3 8EL, in association with Airfix Products Limited, London SW18

Don't forget these other Airfix Magazine Guides!

No 1 *Plastic Modelling*
No 2 *Aircraft Modelling*
No 3 *Military Modelling*
No 4 *Napoleonic Wargaming*
No 5 *Tank and AFV Modelling*
No 6 *RAF Fighters of World War 2*
No 7 *Warship Modelling*
No 8 *German Tanks of World War 2*
No 9 *Ancient Wargaming*
No 10 *Luftwaffe Camouflage of World War 2*
No 11 *RAF Camouflage of World War 2*
No 12 *Afrika Korps*
No 13 *The French Foreign Legion*
No 14 *American Fighters of World War 2*
No 15 *World War 2 Wargaming*
No 16 *Modelling Jet Fighters*
No 17 *British Tanks of World War 2*
No 18 *USAAF Camouflage of World War 2*
No 19 *Model Soldiers*
No 20 *8th Army in the Desert*
No 21 *Modelling Armoured Cars*

Contents

Editor's introduction

This book has been produced as a companion volume to the existing works on German and British tanks of World War 2 (*Airfix Magazine Guides* 8 and 17). However, it has not been possible to make the three books entirely compatible, for various reasons.

The first of these is that it is very difficult to define World War 2 in Soviet terms. It is often forgotten that Russia had been at war almost totally over the period 1918 to 1945, first against the Interventionalist forces immediately after the Russian Revolution up to 1922, then in the far east, particularly against the Japanese, up to 1930; during 1936 and 1937 the Soviets participated in the Spanish Civil War, then in 1938-9 there were two major battles involving tanks against the Japanese (Lake Hassan and River Khalkhin-Gol); in 1939 too the Soviets occupied the Western Ukraine and Belorussia (Poland), then became involved in the Winter War against Finland until 1940. In our terms, however, Soviet involvement in World War 2 proper really begins with the German invasion in 1941, the start of what they call the Great Patriotic War.

Secondly, whereas the Germans had some well-defined starting point with respect to armour development with the rise to power of the Nazi party, the Soviets had carried out an intensive re-armament programme on a massive scale right from the very start. Add to this the fact that much older Russian equipment was utilised in one way or another throughout the period in question, and that some of the operational, organisational and tactical concepts had roots dating back to the earliest days, and it is obvious that it is necessary to provide a sketch of the total development history of the Soviet armoured arm. Descriptions of the earlier periods have, however, been kept to a minium.

Within this book, therefore, the student of armoured warfare and AFV development can find details of Soviet armoured theory from 1917 onwards, including sections on their command structure; armoured organisation from troop to division, brigade, corps, army and front level; tactical and strategic precepts and practice; armoured operations during World War 2; the development and design of Soviet tanks from the first KS tank of 1920 to the IS-3 of 1945; notes on Russian tank camouflage, tactical markings and slogans; and extensive vehicle data tables.

Couple this with Steve Zaloga's excellent 1:76 scale four-view plans and the dozens of photographs, and you have probably the best introductory guide to a very complex subject ever compiled for the use of military and AFV enthusiasts, modellers and wargamers.

BRUCE QUARRIE

one

Soviet armoured tactics and organisation

The Civil War

According to Soviet sources, the earliest official record pertaining to the formation of Soviet armoured units is dated November 1917. It was then that the Provisional Armoured Board was established under the direction of G.V. Elinim. The first task assigned to this board was the convocation of the 2nd All-Russian Armoured Car Conference for the purpose of creating armoured units for the Armed Forces of the new Soviet State.*

After thorough examination by the delegates at the conference, a scheme was approved stating that 'The direction of all amoured units in the Soviet Russian Republic. . .shall be entrusted to the Armoured Units Council subordinated to the Executive Committee selected at the 2nd All-Russian Armoured Car Conference.'

The Armoured Units Council was made organic to the central command apparatus of the Red Army. It remained the basic organ for the direction of armoured units until the end of August 1918, at which time it was transformed into the Armoured Directorate and made subordinate to the Head of the Main Military-Engineering Directorate.

The origin of the formation of Soviet tank units dates back to 1919 when the Armoured Directorate, responding to orders from the RVSR (Revolutionary Military Council) began to put into practice measures for the creation of Soviet tank units. For the first tank units, referred to at that time as Auto-Tank Detachments, use was made of captured tanks taken by the Red Army from the White Armies and the Internationalist forces. By the end of 1919 the Soviet Army disposed of three types of captured tanks, then referred to as 'bolishie' (large), 'srednie' (medium) and 'malie' (small). One tank of each type was made organic to each auto-tank detachment.

The establishment tables for the auto-tank detachment were endorsed by the RVSR on May 28 1920. Shortly afterwards a special detachment was introduced into the unit's establishment totalling 20 soldiers, intended for the protection of tanks in battle. Later, on the basis of a summary analysis of the initial combat experiences with tanks, the need was recognised for the formation of twin-platoon auto-tank detachments having two vehicles of the same type in each platoon. By September 1920 there were 11 auto-tank detachments in the Red Army.

Subsequently, the manufacture of the first Soviet KS light tanks enabled native vehicles to be adopted by the Soviet Army. The tactical-technical characteristics of these first tanks allowed only the direct support and accompaniment of the infantry when breaking through enemy defences, they being inadequate for the development following the breakthrough.

The personnel of the first Soviet armoured units were recruited from numerous volunteers who had served earlier in the armoured car divisions and armoured trains of the old Tsarist Army. This allowed the selection of the best, the most conscientious, and the most technically competent combat-experienced personnel. The training of tankmen was carried out in the Separate Reserve Division for the Formation of Auto-Tank Detachments. The systematic training of command cadres for the armoured force began in April 1918 with the establishment of intensified armoured courses, on the basis of which, at the beginning of 1919, the Armoured School was formed, representing the first combat-

*The First All-Russian Armoured Car Conference had been held in June 1917 under the direction of the Provisional Government.

The KS tank; the first tank to be adopted by the Soviet Army. The vehicle shown, which was the very first model, was called 'Freedom Fighter Comrade Lenin'.

training organisation for the armoured force of the Red Army.

Once more, in the autumn of 1919, the Higher Military-Automobile School was created, intended for the preparation of military engineers for the armoured force and commanders for taking over the role of leading armoured detachments, armoured trains and auto-tank detachments. At the same time the school represented the most important military science centre at that time for analysing the experience of the war and drawing, on a military science basis, conclusions over the use of armoured forces in future war. At the end of 1919 the Armoured School and the Higher Military-Automobile School were amalgamated into one educational establishment—the Higher Military-Automobile-Armoured School of the Red Army.

As early as January 1919, the *First Instructions on the Combat Utilisation of Armoured Cars and Armoured Trains* were brought into being, and in September 1920 the *Instructions for the Combat Utilisation of Tanks* were published. These represented the very first Soviet tank regulations. Broadly, the instructions determined that the armoured forces at that time represented a subsidiary means of combat, their basic role being to carry out thrusts into the enemy suddenly, in combination with rifle troops and horsed-cavalry.

The armoured forces of the Red Army were used with some success on the fronts during the Civil War, and various kinds of combat actions were carried out by these troops. Together with extensions to the roles of armoured units during battles and operations, and increases in their numbers, improvements took place also in the organisational structure of the central command organisations of the armoured forces. In the spring of 1920, for the Field Staff of the RVSR there was created the 'Office of Inspector of Armoured Units', and for the fronts and armies accordingly the 'Office of Chief of Armoured Units'. These were made responsible for controlling the state and fighting efficiency of the armoured force, combat leadership training and for ensuring the correct deployment of armoured units during battles and operations. As before, the Armoured Directorate retained responsibility for forming new units, for material-technical provision to operational troops and the combat training of rear armoured units.

The availability of these two command organisations for the armoured forces resulted inevitably in certain overlaps in their functions. With the aim of removing such deficiences, by an RVSR Directive dated May 6 1921, the 'Independent Directorate of the Chief of the Armoured Forces of the Red Army' was set up, which was subordinated directly to the 'Chief of Staff of the Red Army' and, as regards provisions, to the 'Commander-in-Chief of Supplies'. This form of central organisation for directing the armoured forces represented the most expedient that could be developed at that time.

Between the wars

The period of intense mechanisation and motorisation, and general building-up of the Red Army, which started during the mid-1920s and continued through to the late 1930s, is one that cannot possibly be covered in any great depth here. A whole spectrum of important and interesting aspects—such as the establishment and development of special schools and research centres, factories, training centres (including the influence of foreign assistance, such as the Germans at Kazan and Voronezh, the Americans in the huge automobile and metallurgy centres, etc) must be either dealt with superficially or ignored completely.

In 1924-1925, during the period of military reform, the organisational structure of the Soviet Armed Forces was established in accordance with available armaments and combat means. All the principles of military doctrine were reflected in the *Provisional Field Service Regulations of the Red Army, 1925* and in the *Provisional Combat Regulations for the Armoured Forces of the Red Army, 1925* in which, on the basis of experience gained during the First World and Civil wars, and the Military Intervention, was stated the theory for the combat use of tanks.

The application of the 'Five-Year Plan for the Development of the Armed Forces' was started by the General Staff of the Red Army in 1927, under the direct leadership of M.N. Tukhachevsky, at that time CIGS RKKA. Basically, the plan was formulated on the following conclusions: 'The decisive means for future armed conflicts appear to be: **a** rifle troops together with powerful artillery; **b** strategic horse-cavalry; **c** aviation.' In general, tanks were not referred to here; this was not unintentional. Soviet industry had barely begun the production of the first native tank (MS-1). The total armoured strength in 1927 amounted to one tank regiment and six auto-armoured divisions, excluding the armoured trains. Their establishment included several tanks of foreign origin.

The final draft for the 'First Five-Year Plan for the Development and Reconstruction of the Armed Forces of the USSR' was sanctioned by the Soviet Government on July 30 1928. It was scheduled for the period 1928-1932. At the end of this Five-Year Plan it was intended to have 1,075 tanks and to have formed three new tank regiments and several separate battalions.

In 1928, in connection with the increased progress in the development of native armoured technology, the forces developed the *Provisional Instructions for the Combat Use of Tanks,* in which were detailed clearly the principles for their utilisation.

At that time it was considered that their combat operations should be carried out purely in the interests of the infantry. In the offensive, two levels of infantry cooperation were permitted: tanks for their direct support, or tanks in advanced echelon. In the first case, the tanks played no independent roles and directly assisted the infantry, operating organically. Each rifle battalion was allotted one to three tank platoons depending on the circumstances. In the second case they operated only in tactical liaison with the infantry (ie just outside of their field of fire and vision), independently overwhelming or destroying artillery, local reserves, command points, centres of resistance and other important objectives. The forward echelons (free-maneouvre groups), comprising each one to two tank companies, were created in rifle regiments of the first echelon.

For the development of the success in the depth of the enemy defences, and to replace tank sub-units which had lost their combat effectiveness, reserve echelons were made available to the divisional commander. In the defence, tanks were intended for counter-attacks and counter-thrusts, wedging-in the enemy defensive positions. Rifle units were ceaslessly instructed in cooperating with tanks.

During 1929, in connection with the progress in the rebuilding of the

The MS-1 light tank; later models had improved armament and better performance.

economy and the accelerated tempo of the industrialisation of the country, the Communist Party gave the RVSR the task of supervising the First Five-Year Plan. It was pointed out here that the Red Army must be more powerful than any potential enemy in three decisive forms of armaments, these being: the air force, artillery and tanks. These orders were issued on July 15 1929. Somewhat earlier, on May 6, the Government endorsed a new schedule for the delivery of tanks during the period of the First Five-Year Plan. Altogether, over this period, the Red Army was to receive 3,500 tanks, three times as many as planned in 1928.

On the basis of the orders it had received, the RVSR approved the formation of the following armoured-tank units by the end of the Five-Year Plan: three mechanised brigades; 30 mixed tank battalions, each with 32 light (T-26) and 34 medium (T-28) tanks; four heavy tank battalions in the RGK*, each having 35 tanks; and 13 mechanised regiments for the cavalry, each made up of tank and armoured divisions.

The General Staff of the RKKA demanded the verification, through trial studies, of the most expedient establishment for a tank battalion: primarily, whether it should be mixed or homogeneous. Tanks were not to be included in rifle formations.

Apparently, the RVSR proposed the creation of major tank units in the RGK, intended for augmenting the thrusting power of the rifle formations. Again, since horsed-cavalry at that time was considered to be a decisive means of developing the breakthrough, it was decided that tanks should enter the establishment of the cavalry formations.

Simultaneously with the determination of the organisational structure of armoured-tank units, on July 17 1929 the RVSR approved the tactical-technical requirements for armoured equipment. During 1929 and the first half of 1930 industry began the serial delivery of the MS-1 tank. By the end of 1931 the Army had received nearly 900 of these combat vehicles.

Rapid development of the tactics of the tank troops took place during the 1930s. The accelerated industrialisation of the country permitted the re-equpping of the Army with new tanks and armaments in mass. The impetus to tank production began during the second half of 1931 and proceeded particularly successfully during 1932 and subsequent years. During 1931 the delivery of MS-1 tanks was terminated and production started on the T-26 machine-gun tank and the T-27 tankette. In 1932 the BT-2 tank was adopted, and in 1933 the T-35, T-28, BT-5, T-26 gun tank—in place of the original machine-gun model—and the T-37 amphibious tankette were turned out. From 1932 the Red Army received more than 3,000 tanks and tankettes yearly.

In accordance with the Revvoensovet decision, in 1930 new armoured-tank units and formations

*RGK = the High Command Reserve.

The twin-turreted version of the T-26 light tank. Shown here is the commander's model with frame aerial and a short 37 mm gun in the nearside turret.

began to be formed. On the basis of the small mechanised regiment deployed in the Moscow Military District, the First Experimental-Organisation Mechanised Brigade was created. Placed under the command of K.B. Kalinovsky, it became known as 'Brigade Kalinovsky'. Initially it comprised one MS-1 tank regiment, a motorised infantry regiment, an artillery division and a reconnaissance battalion. The brigade had 60 tanks, 32 tankettes, 17 armoured cars, 264 automobiles and 12 tractors. In 1931 it was intensified, and now comprised: **a** A Reconnaissance Group—a regiment, incorporating a tankette battalion, an auto-armoured division, an auto-machine-gun battalion, and an artillery division; **b** A Thrust Group—a regiment comprising two tank battalions and two self-propelled artillery divisions. For experiments, the self-propelled guns were represented by tractors mounting 76 mm field guns; **c** A battalion of transported infantry; and **d** Artillery groups comprising three divisions (with 76 mm guns and 122 mm howitzers) and an anti-aircraft division. Altogether, the composition of the brigade was placed at 4,700 men, 119 tanks, 100 tankettes, 15 armoured cars, 63 self-propelled anti-aircraft mountings (machine-gun) 32 self-propelled 76 mm guns, 16 122 mm howitzers, 12 76 mm anti-aircraft guns, 32 37 mm anti-aircraft guns, 270 motor-cars and lorries, and 100 tractors.

In peacetime the 'separate tank battalions of the RGK' were deployed as regiments (each with three tank battalions). By mid-1932 four regiments had been formed: the 1st in Smolensk, the 2nd in Leningrad, the 4th in Kharkov. The 3rd Tank Regiment was already in existence in the Moscow Military District as a tank-cadre.

Separate tank battalions were established as territorial units, mainly in industrial regions. By 1932 there were three territorial tank battalions.

Tank units in the horsed-cavalry developed gradually. Initially, there were established three mechanised squadrons and divisions, and later regiments also. By 1932, in the cavalry

The T-27 tankette. Tanks of this type were the very first to be carried by air.

formations there were two mechanised regiments, two divisions and three squadrons.

The rapid developments in aviation and artillery also allowed the possibility of combat inter-cooperation between all arms simultaneously. In this way Soviet military thought developed the ideas of battles and operations in depth expounded earlier by Fuller and Liddel Hart. It was decided that 'the main and fundamental aim of the military art—(is) to forbid the formation of a solid front, to encourage operations and battles which deal a crushing blow and allow a rapid tempo' (Marshal A.I. Egorov). It was considered that the most effective solution was to facilitate a thrust by enormous strike forces to the entire depth of the combat and operative structure of the enemy. And for this it would be necessary to deeply echelon inter-cooperative masses of rifle troops, tanks and artillery, supported by aircraft.

During 1931, and at the beginning of 1932, lively debates took place in the Narkomate for Defence* over the extent and direction of the further expansion of the Soviet Armed Forces, and on their technical requirements. It was recognised that the composition of the Army, which could be deployed in the event of war, would not conform to the tasks that might confront it. Furthermore, the complex theories of

*Narkomate is a contraction of Narodniy Komissariat, which means People's Commissariat.

T-28 tanks of the DD (Distant Action) Group during exercises.

deep penetrations and battles necessitated new methods of approach to the building-up of the Army, in particular, to the mobile troops. In a series of works and papers, originated by M.N. Tukhachevsky and others, a case was argued for the creation then, in peacetime, of large-scale armoured-tank formations with which, in case of war, one could create alongside cavalry formations 'horsed-cavalry-mechanised-armies (groups)' for developing the success during front operations.

At the beginning of August 1931, the government endorsed a plan for the building-up of the RKKA over the period 1931-1933. Simultaneously with this, on August 1 1931, the Council for Labour and Defence accepted the so-called 'Great Tank Programme' which arose from the fact that 'technical achievements in the field of tank construction in the USSR created a sound basis for radical alterations to the universal operative-tactical doctrines in the employment of tanks and necessitated decisive organisational changes to the armoured-tank troops in respect of the creation of superior mechanised formations, capable as much of solving tasks on the battlefield as also in the entire operative depth of a modern combat front. The new high-mobility material of the units provide the basis for elaborating the theories of battles and operations in depth' (M.N. Tukhachevsky).

In order to determine the organisation for armoured-tank troops, a special commission was established which, during a conference held on March 9 1932, recommended that the Soviet Army should possess: **a** Mechanised Corps—comprising mechanised brigades; **b** Tank Brigades of the RGK; **c** Mechanised Regiments in Horsed-Cavalry; and **d** Tank Battalions in Rifle Divisions.

The RVS, on March 11 1932, considered the question of the organisation of the armoured-tank troops and decided to form, in 1932, two mechanised corps for which were selected one rifle division each from the Leningrad and Ukraine Military Districts.

During autumn 1932, on the basis of the 11th Rifle Division in the Leningrad Military District, the 11th Mechanised Corps was formed and, correspondingly, in the Ukraine Military District, on the basis of the 45th Rifle Division, the 45th Mechanised Corps.

In the establishment of the mechanised corps was a mechanised brigade with T-26 tanks (three tank battalions, a rifle-machine-gun battalion, an artillery division, an engineer battalion, an anti-aircraft machine-gun company); a second tank brigade of identical composition but equipped with BT tanks; a rifle brigade; and finally corps units—reconnaissance, engineers, flame-throwing battalions, an anti-aircraft artillery division, a traffic-control company, a technical supply base and an aviation detachment.

During the same year, in accordance with the plan, five separate mechanised brigades, two tank regiments, 12 mechanised regiments, four mechanised divisions for horsed-cavalry, 15 tank and 65 tankette battalions for rifle divisions, began to be formed.

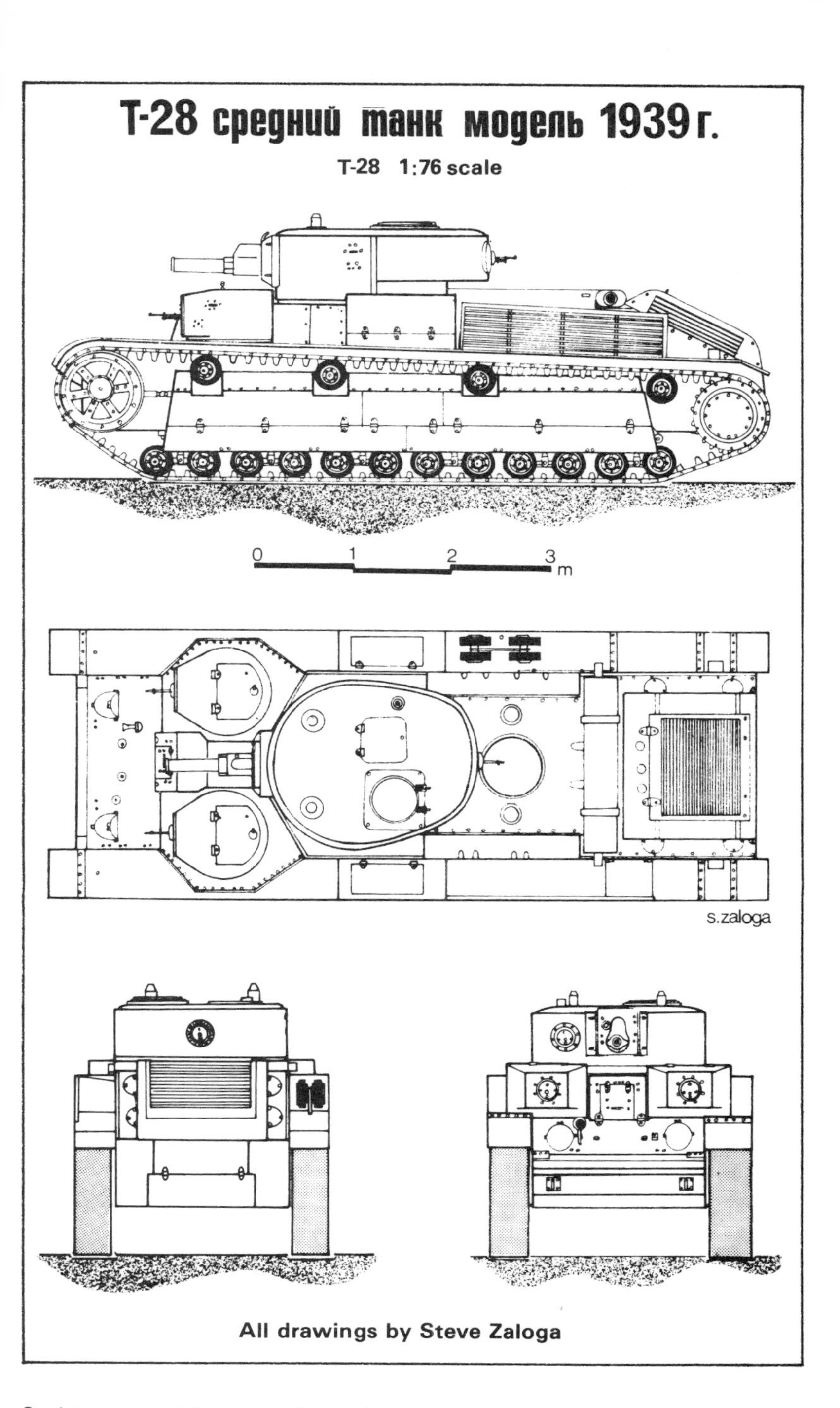

All drawings by Steve Zaloga

It was decided to create further mechanised brigades—the 2nd, for the Ukrainian Military District, the 3rd, 4th and 5th for the Belorussian, and the 6th for the Separate Red-Banner Far-Eastern Army under the command of Marshal Blyukher.

The formation of mechanised troops continued also during 1933. By January 1 1934 in the Army there were two mechanised corps, six mechanised brigades, six tank regiments, 23 tankette battalions and 37 separate companies for rifle divisions, 14 mechanised regiments and five mechanised divisions for cavalry. The completion of these tank formations and units, however, remained at a low level and reached only 47 per cent of the required establishment.

In 1933 a plan was compiled for the development of the RKKA under the Second Five-Year Plan, envisaging a considerable growth in the armoured-tank troops. By January 1 1938 it was planned to have 25 mechanised and tank brigades (including those in mechanised corps). Tank regiments were to be reformed into tank brigades. In a resolution of the Council for Labour and Defence, dated August 13 1933, it was stated that 'under the Second Five-Year Plan it is necessary to reach such a level of Army mechanisation that will allow the mechanised troops to become one of the basic, decisive elements in combat operations'. This resolution entailed a new system of tank application.

The single-turreted model of the T-26 light tank, often referred to as the T-26B. The final version of the tank, also single turreted, was designated T-26S and had sloped, welded armour.

In 1934 a further two mechanical corps were created. In the Leningrad Military District the 7th Mechanised Corps was formed. The 1st Mechanised Brigade in the Moscow Military District was transformed into the 5th Mechanised Corps incorporating the earlier K.B. Kalinovsky Brigade.

In the combined-arms battle tanks were to begin their assigned role as the spearhead force. The tactics of tank troops in the various phases of battle were as follows:

In the offensive

Tanks were used in mass for the breakthrough, in cooperation with aviation, infantry and artillery, pursuing their aims by operations and battles at a high tempo.

Based on the tactical-technical characteristics of the T-26 light tank it was considered that, for the simultaneous overpowering of the enemy, it was necessary to have one tank per infantry machine-gun and two to three per anti-tank gun. Consequently, in order to destroy the enemy on the frontal perimeter, it was necessary for each kilometer of front to have 15-16 NPP (Direct Infantry-Support) tanks; against the company of the second echelon eight or nine light tanks from the DPP (Distant (Remote) Infantry-Support Group), which would operate in the depth of the defences. For successfully combating the enemy artillery one company of medium tanks would be allocated to each battery. In order to crush the divisional artillery, it was necessary to have six companies or two battalions of medium tanks (T-28), comprising the DD (Distant Action Group), backed up by one artillery division (all 12 batteries).

Such a procedure as the use of a rifle company to break through the defensive zone of an enemy infantry division on an 8 km front, simultaneously occupying his entire depth, demanded the use of 180 NPP tanks, ie 3-4 light tank battalions; one to two DPP tank battalions, and two battalions of medium DD tanks.

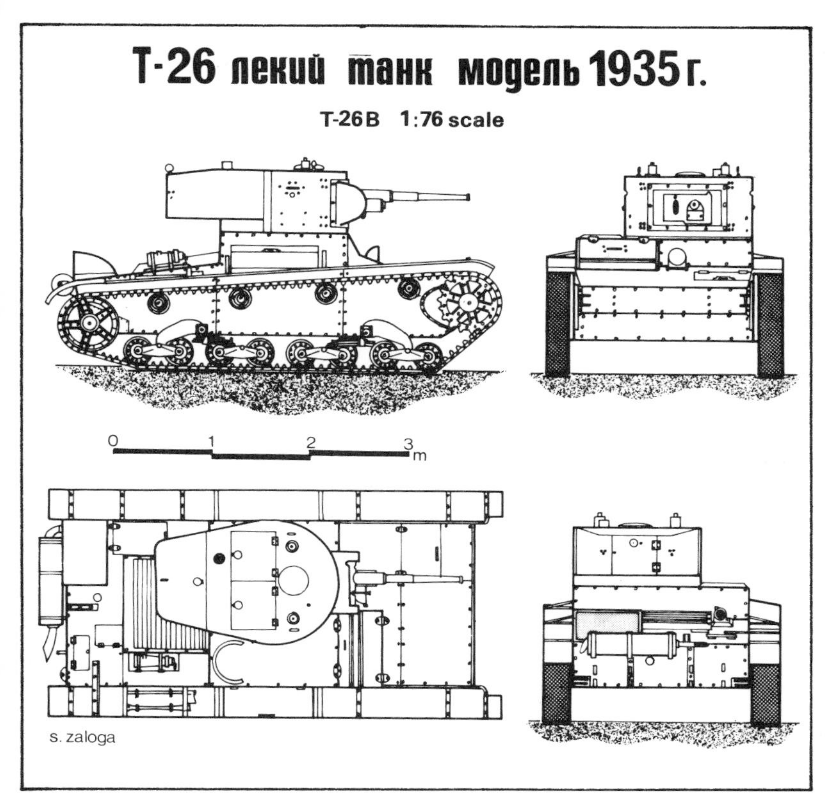

Tank Groups For the Direct Support of Infantry (Cavalry) These had the task of providing a path for the attacking infantry (or cavalry) to the entire depth of the offensive, acting in close cooperation with it. The tanks cleared a passage through barbed-wire obstacles, destroyed enemy machine-guns and active forces as well as his anti-tank means, at the same time repelling counter-attacks. Attacking in combat lines with intervals of 25-30 m, they 'hugged' the artillery fire barrage. The infantry moved with the tanks in lines, not falling behind by more than 100 m. On meeting obstacles or rather difficult sectors, rifle sub-units would move forward and put in an attack, under the covering fire of the tanks. The engineers assisted in the provision of passages. Overcoming the obstacles, tanks once more advanced ahead of the infantry and led the way. Inter-cooperational and instructional signals were established between tanks, infantry and artillery.

Tank Groups For the Distant (Remote) Support of Infantry (Cavalry) These were intended for suppressing the firepower means and active forces in the immediate tactical depth of the defences, and operated in cooperation with the infantry and the NPP tanks to a depth of 2-4 km. Concurrently with the attack by the DPP tanks (H-hour) they would break through into the depth of the defences and begin the destruction of appointed objectives with such precision as to render impossible any support by them to the sub-units defending the frontal perimeter. This, it was conceived, would enable a fast rate of advance.

Tanks For Distant Action These were intended primarily for the destruction of divisional and corps artillery as well as divisional HQs and the immediate operative reserves committed to the counter-attack.

DD tanks would independently break through the frontal defensive perimeter about 20-30 minutes before H-hour, arriving in the appointed area with such precision as to be able to begin a combined attack against enemy artillery units and other important objectives thereby distracting them from

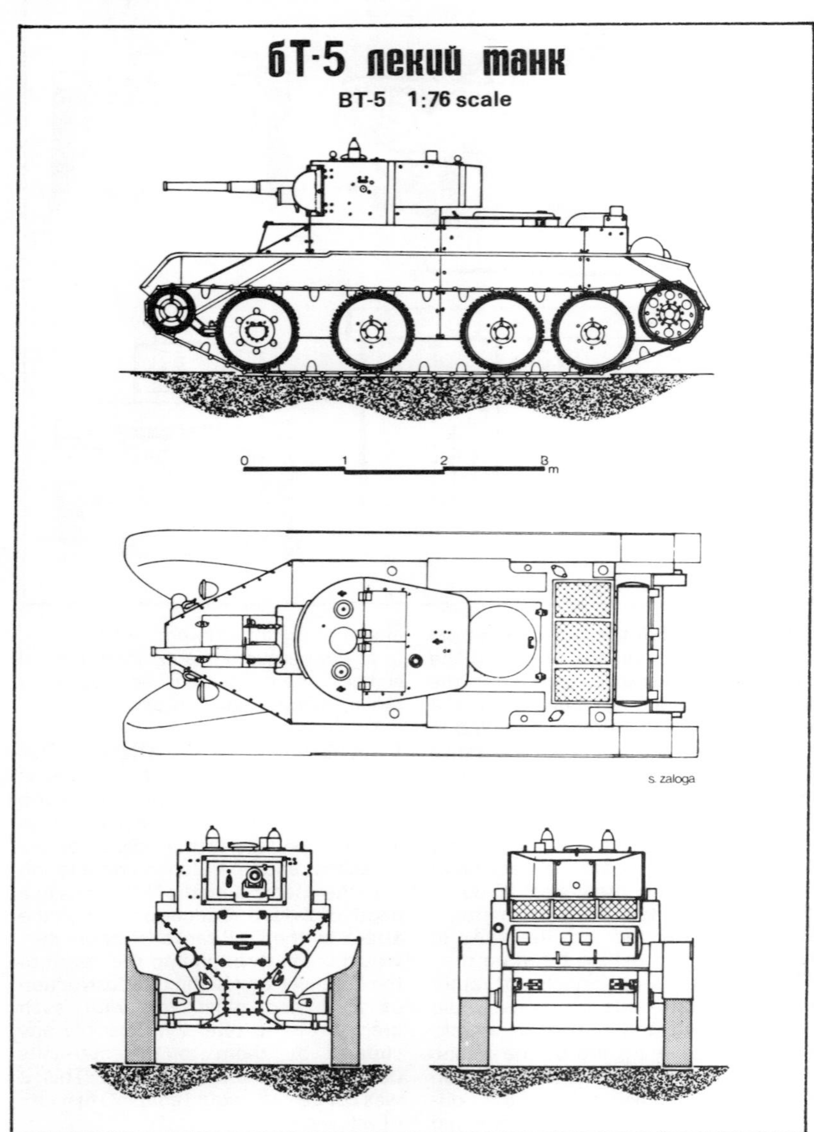

their assigned tasks. Simultaneously, some three to six artillery batteries would engage the enemy.

Aircraft, cooperating with the TDD, would reveal to them any anti-tank means, artillery batteries and other enemy objectives, and also carry out specific tasks such as informing the tank commanders of the most advantageous directions from which to attack. Immediately prior to the attack, the aircraft would execute bombing and strafing missions against the enemy points of resistance.

Thus it was considered that, during the 'battle in depth', DD, DPP and NPP tank groups, 'echeloning forward', could carry out most important roles. In connection with this, in particular it was considered that the successful penetration of the defences at a high rate (2.5-3 kph) could only be achieved when along the direction of the main thrust tanks were used in mass—with a density of 75-100 vehicles per kilometer of front. It was considered that, given these conditions, six or seven hours would be sufficient in order to break through the tactical defensive zone and 'open the gates' to the depth.

The principles of battles and operations in depth were persistently introduced into practical combat training. Of great significance in this respect were the large-scale military manoeuvres carried out over the period 1935-36 in the Moscow, Belorussian and Kiev Military Districts.

Whilst these Soviet views on the conduct of the mechanised offensive were reasonably sound for those times, the tremendous emphasis placed on precision and coordination and the pure size of the units involved (often corps level) required a very high level of technological communications which just did not exist at that time.

In meeting engagements or encounter battles

Quite correctly, the Soviets determined that the mobile character of future wars inferred large encounter battles and meeting engagements which, by their very nature, entailed the fullest use of tank troops possessing mobility, firepower and thrusting force. In the instructional literature of those years it was emphasised that encounter battles were characteristic of fierce struggles to gain the initiative, of striving to impose one's will upon the enemy—destroying him through the seizure of advantageous objectives, by opening fire and developing decisive thrusts on the flanks and rear of the enemy before he could deploy, by pursuing him to the ultimate defeat. The obscurity of the conditions accompanying this type of battle necessitated that commanders at all levels should make well-timed, bold and intelligent decisions regarding the destruction of even small enemy forces. It was recommended that the order of march be organised in such a way that it represented implicitly the future form of battle order.

In the defensive

The contemporary Soviet defence was based upon a system of anti-infantry and anti-tank fire combined with

The BT-7 wheel/track tank, second model, negotiating an anti-tank ditch during the Kiev manoeuvres.

the use of the most advantageous terrain, heavily fortified buildings and obstacles, and upon the counter-attack and counter-thrust by the second echelon with the aim of routing or 'wedging-in' the enemy. The main objective was to bring about his defeat in front of the FEBA. To achieve this, no less than two-thirds of the firepower were to be made available for the creation of an 'impenetratable fire zone', some 400-600m in depth. However, the massed use of tanks in the offensive necessitated also their mass use in the defensive so that, should the enemy break through in depth, he could be worn down and then counter-attacked. The execution of defensive tasks involved the defeat of enemy tanks and their supporting infantry so long as a serious threat existed.

Tank sub-units comprising the 'manoeuvre thrust reserve of the combined-arms commander' would frequently be used in combination with second-echelon divisions (regiments) for the liquidation of the wedged-in enemy and thereby restore the defence.

Experiments, carried out with mechanised corps, showed them to be cumbersome and to have low mobility. Due to poor means of communication, particularly with respect to radio equipment, corps commanders could not cope with the control of subordinate units. The corps were slow-moving during the advance march and when conducting breaks-through. This was due to the poor reliability of certain tank components, to the poor technical ability of personnel comprising a significant proportion of the tanks, and also to the poor state of the roads. After 1935 the formation of new corps was stopped.

On November 28 1937 a plan was approved for the development and reconstruction of the Red Army over the period 1938-1941, the Fourth Five-Year Plan. Therein no increase in the number of tank formations was envisaged; to be retained were four corps, 21 separate tank brigades, three separate armoured brigades and, in place of a cadre brigade, 11 tank (training) regiments were to be formed. The combat element of the brigade, however, was strengthened considerably by changing over from three to five-tank platoons. The light tank brigade, on establishment, comprised 278 BT tanks, and brigades equipped with T-26 tanks had 267. Heavy brigades had, on establishment, 183 tanks (of which 136 were T-28s, 37 BTs, and ten flame-throwing), and T-35 brigades—148 tanks (of which 94 were T-35s, 44 BTs and ten flame-throwing). Tank regiments were intended to have from 190 to 267 tanks.

In the establishment of each rifle division tank battalions of twin-company composition were introduced (T-26 and T-28), and in each cavalry division a tank regiment.

In accordance with the plan, in 1938 the armoured-tank troops received a new organisation. With the aim of eliminating unnecessary divisions in nomenclature between mechanised and tank, one name—tank—was adopted for all armoured-tank formations and units. Brigades having BT and T-26 tanks were called light-tank, and those with T-28 and T-35 heavy-tank. On establishment, light-tank brigades comprised four tank battalions with 54 standard (gun) and six artillery tanks (armed with 76.2 mm guns) in each, reconnaissance, a motor-rifle battalion and supply sub-units. In brigades equipped with T-28 and T-35 tanks, the platoons remained tri-tank. Accordingly, the mechanised corps was renamed the tank corps. Tank brigades, comprising the corps, received the same organisational structure as the separate light-tank brigades.

The combat operations in which the Red Army participated during 1938-1939 revealed certain deficiencies in troop organisation. (The tank troops experienced a partial examination during the battles with the Japanese at Lake Khasan during 1938 and on the River Khalkhin-Gol in 1939, and also during the Russo-Finnish War of 1939-40.) The continual increases in anti-tank means for the defence

The T-35 heavy tank in action during winter operations.

brought about changes in the views on the combat use of tanks with infantry during the offensive. In order to study these factors and to provide recommendations for their improvement, in July 1939 the Main Military Council set up a commission under the chairmanship of Deputy Commissar for Defence, G.I. Kulik, which sat from August 8 to 22 1939. During discussions over the organisation of the tank troops, a controversy developed in connection with the opinions of Chief of the Auto-Armoured Directorate, Corps Commander D.G. Pavlov. Pavlov commented on the unsuitability of retaining the tank corps. He argued on the experience of the combats in Spain, of which he was a participant, that the use of corps for 'raiding' in the enemy rear was impermissible since it excluded such a possibility as breaking through an enemy front. Here it would be impossible, he said, to develop the success using a too cumbersome tank corps (according to the 1938 establishment the corps was intended to have 560 tanks and 12,710 men). Apart from this, for success in any offensive operation, tanks needed strong infantry, artillery and aviation support. The tank corps commander, in his opinion, could never manipulate all of these means in strength.

The majority of the members of the committee, however, voted in favour of retaining the corps. The commission advocated two types of tank brigade: for independent action—brigades equipped with BT tanks; and for reinforcing rifle troops—brigades equipped with T-26 and T-28 tanks. During November 1939 the Main Military Council considered the proposals of the commission, but all the same agreed on the necessity of disbanding the tank corps and the rifle-machine-gun brigades organic to the corps.

This decision may be taken as the greatest blunder in Soviet military history and almost immediately after the disaster following the German attack on June 22 1941, Pavlov was shot. Nevertheless, certain important factors ought to be taken into account. Mention has already been made concerning the difficulties of liaison and communication. Before giving its decision, the Main Military Council (chaired by Iosef Stalin* himself) examined thoroughly the experience gained with the corps during the Russo-Finnish War, and even more recently during the march by the Red Army into the western regions of Belorussia and the Ukraine in September 1939. In this latter campaign two corps took part—the 15th Tank (from the Belorussian Military District) and the 25th Tank (Ukrainian Military District). The commanders of these corps found great difficulty in directing their subordinate brigades, as the result of which the corps even lagged behind the cavalry divisions.

*The Russian spelling of 'Joseph' is 'Iosef', and has been used throughout this book, eg IS-2, ISU-152 not JS-2, etc.

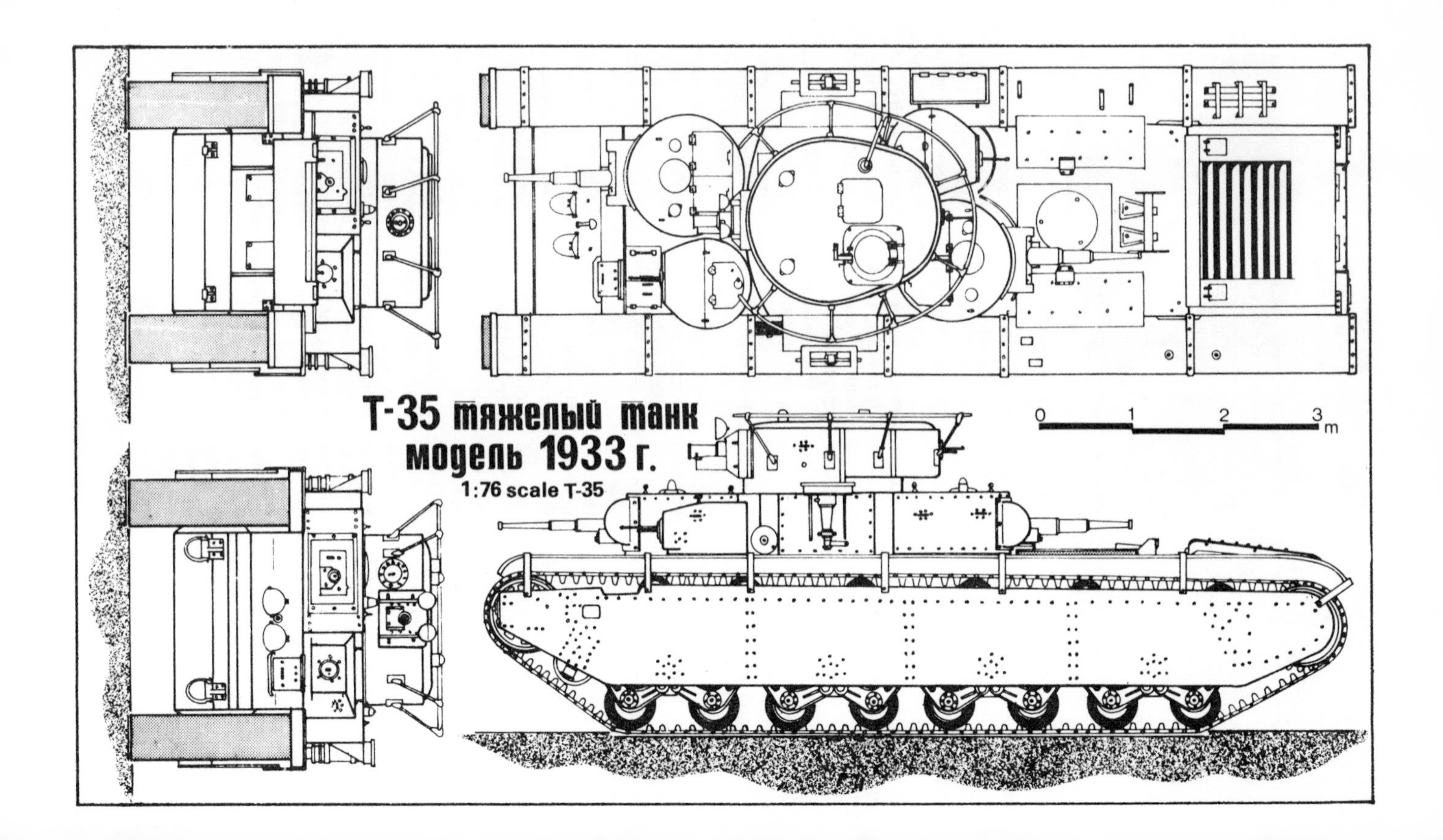
T-35 тяжелый танк
модель 1933 г.
1:76 scale T-35
0
1
2
3
m

The breaking-down of the corps was, on Soviet admission, a retrograde step in the evolution of the tank forces. As a matter of fact, it was a drastic departure from the basic principles of combat and operations in depth, since not only was the possibility of using large, centralised masses of armour removed, but it became extremely difficult to instill any clarity of purpose in the training of commanders and staffs for operational scale missions.

In a directive dated November 21 1939, the Main Military Council ordered the replacement of the corps by motorised divisions (with the disbandment of the corps the tank brigade represented the highest armoured echelon). It was planned to form 15 motorised divisions, eight in 1940 and seven during the first half of 1941. On establishment the division was scheduled to have 258 BT tanks and 17 T-37/T-40 light amphibious tanks, making a total of 275 (20 of these being in the divisional reserve), 11,650 men, 98 guns and mortars (over 50 mm calibre) and 49 armoured cars. It was to be made up of two motor-rifle, one tank and one artillery regiments; reconnaissance, liaison and light engineer battalions; divisional anti-tank, anti-aircraft, and also supply units. The directive foresaw re-equipping the tank troops with the new T-34 tanks in place of the BT-7s.

The organisation of a motorised division was a better prospect than that of the earlier existing corps. The motorised division was intended for use as an echelon to develop the successes of combined-arms armies and also for integration into the horsed-cavalry-mechanised groups.

Alongside the motorised divisions, for reinforcing corps, tank brigades were also to be retained. Altogether, it was planned to have 32 brigades and ten tank regiments, to be developed into brigades during wartime. Thereby BT and T-26 brigades, on establishment, were intended to have 258 tanks, and T-28 and T-35 brigades, 156 tanks.

In 1940 motorised divisions began to be organised. By May of that year four had been formed. During June 1940, in the Narkomate for Defence, an examination was conducted on the experiences of combat operations by German troops in the west, the results of which were reported to Stalin. On his orders the decision was taken to form, in the Red Army, mechanised corps comprising 1,000 to 1,200 tanks. In other words this was almost a complete reversal of the directive issued during December 1939. The corps were intended to have two tank divisions, a motorised division of the December 5 1939 establishment, a motor-cycle regiment, separate liaison and motorised engineer battalions, and also an aviation squadron. The tank division was to be composed of two tank, one motor-rifle and one artillery regiments and various sub-units for combat and material supply. The division was envisaged to have 11,343 men, 413 tanks (of which 105 were to be KVs, 210 T-34s, 26 BT-7s, 18 T-26s and 54 flame-throwing), 91 armoured cars, and 58 guns and mortars (over 50 mm calibre). The motorised division incorporated two motorised, one tank, and one artillery regiments, together with various support elements. The total corps table of organisation called for from 1,025 to 1,108 tanks, 126 of which were KVs, 420 T-34s, and the remainder either BT-7s or T-26s. The total manpower was put at 37,200 men (under wartime establishment).

Through a resolution by the Council of People's Commissars dated July 6 1940, these organisations for mechanised corps and the tank division were accepted. In the Red Army it was planned to have eight corps and two separate tank divisions.

During the second half of 1940, on the basis of a number of rifle and cavalry corps organisations having motorised, cavalry and rifle divisions and tank brigades, there began to be formed: in the Leningrad Military District—the 1st Mechanised Corps; in the Western Special Military District—the 3rd and 6th; in the Kiev Special Military District—the 4th and 8th; in Odessa—the 2nd; in the Transbaikal—the 5th; in the Moscow district—the 7th corps; and in the Transcaucasus and

T-37 light amphibious tanks during water-borne exercises. Due to the absence of radio on these tanks, the commander is communicating by means of a flag. Unit commander's tanks were fitted with long-range radio equipment.

Central-Asian districts—each one independent tank division (6th and 9th respectively). At the end of the year, in the Kiev Special Military District a further additional one was created—the 9th Mechanised Corps. At the beginning of 1941 the organisation of the tank regiment in the tank division was revised with respect to decreasing the quantity of heavy tanks from 52 to 31. Accordingly, this decreased the number of tanks in the division from 413 to 375. It was with this establishment that the corps entered the Great Patriotic War.*

In 1940 the new mechanised corps organisation was accepted without any experimental verification. The means of communication, allocated to the corps, were the same as for the 1939 corps, ie the 71 TK tank radio and the 5AK automobile station. With such radio equipment it turned out that the corps commander could not cope even with the control of the earlier organisation having only 560 tanks. Even so, despite even more complex conditions the commanders preferred the new corps, in which the quantity of tanks had increased to practically double.

In February 1941 the Government approved the new measures to be taken to strengthen the Red Army. Apart from the nine mechanised corps already in existence, it was planned to form, during the course of 1941, a further 21 corps. For their formation all tank units, including the tank battalions in the rifle divisions, were to be used. Tanks were to be retained only by cavalry divisions (each having a tank regiment with 64 BT-ts) and by air-landing corps (each having a tank battalion with 50 T-38 and T-40 tanks).

Nevertheless, by the outbreak of war (June 22 1941) the majority of mechanised corps had not yet been completed; some had no tanks at all and a few lacked tank crews. At the beginning of the war there were 29 activated mechanised corps, 31 motorised and 61 tank divisions.

*In Russian military literature the term 'Great Patriotic War' is used to separate the operations on the Eastern Front, from June 22 1941, from all other operations preceding that and running concurrently in other theatres.

The Great Patriotic War 1941-1945

As may be discerned from the previous section, on the eve of the war the Soviet armoured-tank and mechanised troops were to be found in a process of extensive reorganisation and rearmament. The mechanised corps were not fully established as regards both equipment and personnel. The tanks with which they were equipped were mostly out of date and the new KV and T-34 tanks deployed in the Western military districts totalled only about 1,500.

The pre-war theory for the utilisation of armoured-tank and mechanised troops once more became the basis for operations. It was considered as fundamental to develop the offensive in great depth and at a rate of up to 80 km per day by acting in the operative depth of the enemy defences. The Soviets state, however, that it was extremely difficult for them to apply this theory practically when under conditions of an enforced strategic withdrawal.

During the first phase of the war, the Soviet armoured forces suffered huge losses (lowest estimate 17,500—highest 24,000 tanks). The reasons for this are extremely varied and complex, and to provide a clear picture it would be necessary to go into a lengthy, protracted discussion. Nevertheless, on the tank side, a few critical points may be expounded to give some idea of the general situation.

In the first instance, the Soviet armoured forces were at the beginning of an overall rearmament cycle. The bulk of their equipment had been designed in 1931-32 with the contemporary level of technology and to conform to the general philosophy of tank warfare at that time. This equipment was in a process of replacement when the Germans attacked.

Secondly, the organisational, tactical and strategical (operational) procedures of the Soviet armoured forces also were in a state of major upheaval, resulting from a realignment to the large-scale tank formations. At the time when the Germans attacked, many Soviet units were in transit, often separated from their equipment, and few really knew where they were meant to go. Even the General Staff had no idea where some of the units were, or even destined for.

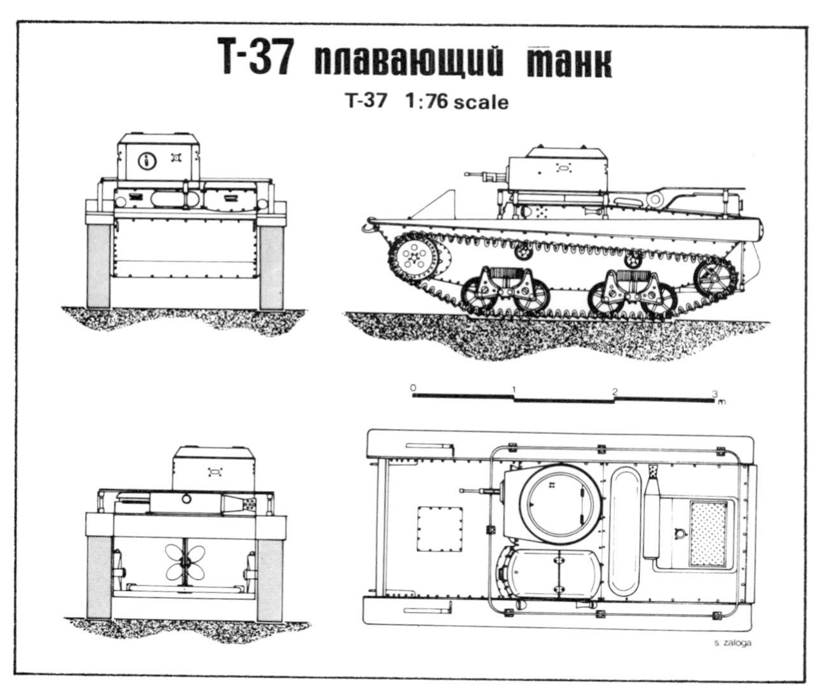

Thirdly, the Great Purge of 1937-38 had greatly weakened both the Soviet Officer Corps and the nucleus of professional and experienced men. Rapid field promotions resulted and many tank crews had only a few hours' gunnery or driving experience.

Fourthly, and very significant, the Army had been given a blanketing order from the highest levels of command (Stalin) for 'No Provocation!' Reports from the front on June 22 1941 of sudden German attacks were interpreted as 'incidents' to provoke the Russians. It was not until whole brigades or corps had actually been committed that the High Command began to take matters seriously. By then it was too late—invariably large sections of the Army had been encircled or out-manoeuvred. Fuel and ammunition depots, located in the border districts, had been overrun and a large quantity of vehicles destroyed or captured.

During the first days of the war, the mechanised corps deployed in the western border districts became engaged in fierce encounter battles with the German panzer divisions. Two of these corps were then deployed in the Baltic, five in the Western, and eight in the Kiev Military Districts. They were either being phased into combined-arms armies or remained under the direct jurisdiction of the district commander. In accordance with their training they attempted to insert counter-thrusts upon the main enemy groups that were penetrating into the depths of Russia. Some of these counter-thrusts were effective, but most were not. One mechanised corps on the South-Western Front, engaged in a fierce battle with the German 1st Tank Group, succeeded in delaying its advance in the Zhitomir-Kiev direction by several days. After the first counter-thrusts the mechanised corps were ordered to pass over to the defensive, in cooperation with the rifle troops (infantry).

Had the Soviet Army been at a higher state of preparedness it might have repelled the German attacks by 'spoiling actions' or surprise counter-attacks. Not having any clearly defined offensive or defensive grouping of forces, however, it was simply not prepared for any such operations. Combined-arms formations and units at that time lacked sufficient strength and experience to provide an effective defence or to effectively resist massed attacks by large groups of tanks. Under these circumstances, most of the mechanised corps had been assigned missions of carrying out counter-attacks with the object of destroying one or more of the enemy's groups of forces and to win time for organising a stable defence. They seldom achieved their

T-34/76B tank in action at the battle of Moscow. Due to the shortage of supporting vehicles, the Soviets adopted the 'tank descent' tactic whereby accompanying infantry were carried on the tank as shown here.

aims for a variety of reasons—such as lack of opportunity to lay on missions, many of which were clearly beyond their capabilities, lack of intelligence on the situation, lack of coordination, etc.

Attempts were made by several corps to carry out coordinated counter-attacks. This type of operation, however, required strategic formations of tank forces having well-trained staffs and effective means of control which were non-existent in the Red Army at that time. Not having sufficient time to organise counter-attacks and lacking in firm control by senior commanders, the mechanised corps acted as separate units under the most complex and unfavourable of circumstances. Furthermore, within the formations and corps there was no clear-out coordination of operations. Reconnaissance was often poorly conducted, without steps being taken to ensure march and combat security. The handling of POL and ammunition also left much to be desired.

During these critical operations, Soviet tank units and formations usually operated as follows. Sub-units equipped with KVs and T-34s were, as a rule, located in the forward echelon, and were assigned the task of destroying the enemy's PzKpfw III and IV tanks as well as his anti-tank guns. Sub-units equipped with BT and T-26 tanks, making up the second echelon, were deployed against the motorised infantry, armoured carriers and artillery.

Due to the rapidity of the German advance, which threatened the great tank plants in Western Russia, the latter had to be evacuated to the east—principally to the Urals. As the result, the tremendous losses of the early part of the war could not be compensated for until this industry had been rebuilt and in full swing.

Following these tremendous losses in tanks, on July 15 1941 the General Headquarters made a fundamental decision. As the result, the small quantity of tanks still in service with the fronts was now used only for direct cooperation with the infantry. Here, the tanks were used to operate from ambush, to bolster up the infantry in the defence, and for special counter-attacks. These changes in the methods of using tanks necessitated organisational changes to the armoured-tank troops.

From autumn 1941 all mechanised corps and tank divisions (what was left of them) were disbanded. The tank units were assembled into separate formations and assigned to army commanders. Motorised rifle divisions became purely rifle divisions. According to Soviet sources, on December 1 1941 there were only 1,984 tanks deployed with the field army. Under these conditions the basic organisational units for armoured-tank troops became separate tank brigades and separate tank battalions. In the battles which developed during autumn and winter 1941 these were used only for executing tactical, as opposed to operational, tasks, both in defence and in the attack.

According to the Soviets, the absence of large armoured-tank formations in the Soviet Army at that time limited its ability to develop tactical successes in operations and to conduct fast offensives. They provide this as one of the reasons for the failure to exploit certain winter offensives, particularly that at Moscow. This is partly true, but overriding factors were the inexperience on the part of the Soviet High Command, the lack of experienced and well-trained officers at the lower echelons, and the shortage of military transport.

Once more applying their pre-war concepts for the use of tanks, the Soviets maintained that 'the decisive and mobile nature of operations demanded both the operative-tactical and organisational massing of armoured-tank troops.' At the end of 1941 the Battle for Moscow appeared to both sides to be one of the most important of the entire war, which it was. Appointed to the command of the Soviet troops at Moscow was G.K. Zhukov who, given the authority by Stalin personally to concentrate at Moscow practically the entire Soviet tank forces—now somewhat enlarged through new tanks from the Eastern factories, but even more so by the release of a large number of troops and equipment from the Special Far-Eastern Red Banner Army, had the opportunity to apply this theory.

During the defensive stage of the battle, the Soviets employed novel methods of combating numerically superior enemy tank forces, such as the tank ambush. It was essentially this: in the defensive sector of a tank brigade of the first echelon a reinforced motorised battalion was deployed. Under cover of an outpost, it organised a defensive area which appeared to be the real thing, having a false MDR (main defence line) and dummy anti-tank guns, machine-guns and motar positions. The real MDR and firing positions were carefully camouflaged. The fire-plan having been established, manoeuvre by fire and sub-units on the most likely route of advance by the enemy was planned. In the second echelon, areas were chosen for tank ambushes, which were echeloned in depth and had a flank position in relation to the most likely route of advance for enemy tanks. In the ambush itself there was usually a tank platoon—at times, however, there might only be two or even one, tanks. Commanders of battalions and brigades held a tank group in reserve to counter unforeseen attacks. The critical approach route was mined.

Prior to committing his tanks to the attack, the enemy had laid down an artillery preparation. Most of his concentrations in this case fell on the false position.

Motorised rifle sub-units usually allowed the attacking tanks to pass right through their positions so as to cut off and destroy the infantry advancing behind them. Vehicles were destroyed individually by anti-tank grenades and Molotov Cocktails. Tanks that had penetrated deep into the defences were destroyed by the surprise flanking fire of the tank ambush, at a range of about 200-300 m. Having defeated the enemy from one position, the tanks in the ambush quickly transferred to another position to avoid losses from artillery fire and air strikes. The unexpected and effective Soviet fire caused a certain amount of disorder amongst the enemy troops and disrupted their plan of attack. They were under the impression that there was a considerably larger force opposing them than there actually was.

In defensive battles, the basic strength of the tank brigades and battalions was located within the combat formations of rifle units on critical paths of tank approach. A proportion of the tanks, however, occupied positions in combination with anti-tank artillery, rifle and engineer units in anti-tank strongpoints and positions. There were occasions when motorised rifle and tank divisions carried out independent missions in cooperation with rifle and cavalry units.

During the counter-offensive at Moscow some 20 tank brigades and about the same number of battalions were deployed. The main emphasis was placed on the infantry forces; nevertheless, very important missions were carried out by the tank troops. In order to develop the success, improvised mobile groups were created and made organic to certain tank brigades and cavalry formations of a number of combined-arms armies.

Operating in close cooperation with the infantry, NPP tanks provided the means of manoeuvre which successfully turned the German flanks and forced them to withdraw from important lines of defence.

Tanks were often employed in the group of forces of foward detachments, which were sent forward to seize vital objectives or escape routes along the enemy's line of withdrawal.

The role of tanks when deployed in mobile groups is of interest. During the Volokolamsk offensive, for example, two mobile groups were formed by the Commander of the 16th Army: one group from the 145th Tank Brigade, the 44th Cavalry Division and the 17th Rifle Brigade; the other from the 1st Guards and 17th Tank Brigades, the 89th Tank Battalion and the 40th Rifle Brigade. Turning the enemy's flanks at an inward position, they then threatened envelopment, forcing him to begin a withdrawal. Pursuing the enemy, the mobile group raced ahead and, with fighting, managed to free Volokolamsk.

Despite lessons learnt, and the improvements in command tactics, the Soviets continued to make mistakes. They still tended to allocate tanks equally between rifle units (as the result of inadequate intelligence regarding the enemy and terrain), which made it impossible to mass tanks along the main advance routes. They attempted to deeply echelon tanks in direct infantry support, resulting in a deterioration in striking and firepower capab-

Right *Crews of a T-34/76B tank unit preparing for the counter - offensive at Stalingrad, spring 1942.* **Below** *The commander of a T-34/76D unit briefing his tank crews prior to the counter - offensive at Stalingrad.*

ilities. In the offensive tanks would often move too far ahead of the infantry and artillery, and they would be forced to return to them (sometimes several times during a day), thereby suffering unnecessary losses. Subsequently, the General Staff stipulated that tanks in a direct infantry support role should not advance further than 400 m ahead of their accompanying infantry.

Experience gained by the Soviet troops during the counter-offensive before Moscow, and in the other offensive operations of winter 1941-42, was carefully analysed. Based on this analysis, the General Headquarters at first issued a directive and then (on January 22 1942) an order, in which was presented a thorough analysis of past battles, highlighting deficiencies and suggesting methods of avoiding them. On a broad level, the experience

The crew of a T-34/76B tank stocking up with ammunition on the Karelian Front (Finland) 1942. This vehicle has been fitted with extra-wide tracks to cater for the poor terrain/climatic conditions.

convinced the Soviet High Command of the validity of one of the most fundamental principles of their pre-war theory. This was that, 'for the successful execution of an offensive to a great depth and at a fast rate, in addition to separate tank units for cooperation with the infantry, it is necessary to have available large armoured-tank formations organic to the attacking troops, and intended for independent actions.' The execution of this principle in practice, however, required a large number of tanks. For this reason the greatest priority was placed on tank production. As the result 24,668 tanks were produced during 1942, 50.8 per cent being T-34s. According to official Soviet documents the number of tanks deployed in the operative armies was, in May 1942 4,959, and in November 1942 6,956. Apart from the T-34 and KV tanks, production was continued of the T-60 and T-70 tanks. This was not by choice, since the Soviets had already become convinced of the ineffectiveness of the light tank, but it could be produced faster and therefore rendered great assistance to the rifle troops who would have otherwise been left without any tanks at all. With the growth in production of medium tanks, however, their delivery to the troops was discontinued and existing vehicles were converted to self-propelled weapons and armoured support vehicles.

In the meantime, the directive stipulated that separate tank battalions and brigades should be employed in full strength and in close cooperation with infantry, artillery and the air arm. Tanks should not be committed to battle without prior intelligence as to the disposition of the enemy and without reconnaissance of the terrain on which an action was to take place. The artillery was expected to carry out 'artillery offensives', which included artillery preparations for an attack, artillery support during the attack, and the availability of artillery fire to forces advancing deep into the enemy's defences.

By the spring of 1942 the increased production of tanks allowed the

A T-34/76D tank in operation during the actions of spring 1943.

creation of tank corps. Mechanised corps also began to be formed in the autumn. This was not, however, a return to the old corps organisation. The tank corps had three tank and one motor-rifle brigades and incorporated 168 tanks. The tank and mechanised brigades, now having the very latest equipment, formed the corps' organisational basis. The mechanised corps comprised three mechanised and one tank brigades and had 175 tanks. During this period, operational units of tank forces were being mobilised—the tank armies. At first there were two, and these differed little from combined-arms armies. At the end of 1942 the Soviets also began to form heavy-tank regiments.

The first two tank armies (the 3rd and the 5th), formed in April-May 1942, were of mixed composition and made up of tank corps, rifle divisions, cavalry formations, artillery and mortar units, and various supporting sub-units. In the views of the Soviet High Command they were intended for independently breaking through prepared enemy defences and for developing the success in operations.

The tank corps and tank armies were used for the first time during the summer of 1942. Amongst other operations, they participated in the Kharkov operation on the South-Western Front where the Soviet Army was conducting defensive actions; during the battle on the Bryansk Front; on the Voronezh Front, and on the avenues of approach to Stalingrad.

During the early days, with lack of experience, the Soviets made many mistakes in deploying these corps and armies. At times they were committed to battle at the wrong moment, or given assignments outside of the unit's capabilities, or were thrown into battle piecemeal rather than integral. There was still lack of experience on the part of the Command nucleus and staff when planning and organising combat operations at short notice, when controlling forces during meeting engagements, under rapidly changing and complex conditions, and inadequate coordination of action within their own combat elements and with respect to other combat and supporting arms. Drastic measures were taken in an attempt to eliminate these deficiencies. Command cadres, staffs and large numbers of tank crews had to be trained. This was successfully carried out. The manoeuvrability and mobility of the units improved, and their aptitude for tactical and operational coordinated action with other combat arms and services also increased.

Awareness of these errors, coupled with the combat experience gained during the 1942 battles, enabled the Soviet High Command to determine new principles for utilising the corps in future battles and operations, and these were set out in NKO Order No 325, dated October 16 1942. According

T-34/76D tanks during the summer 1943 operations.

to this, separate tank brigades and regiments were to be used for the direct support of infantry, and tank and mechanised corps were to be made available to fronts* and armies for use along the main direction as 'echelons for the development of the success'. The latter were to insert powerful thrusts with the aim of cutting off and encircling large enemy groups.

*The Soviets have a special term, 'front', which has no counterpart in other armies. It means a group of armies deployed under a central command on a particular sector. An army itself is a group of corps.

The basic points of the order were put into practice during the counter-offensive at Stalingrad. In this battle the armoured-tank and mechanised troops became the basic thrust force of the land troops. 15 tank and mechanised corps were used in this operation, and during the course of the counter-offensive they were used as echelons for the development of the success by the Army, attacking along the main direction. They were usually introduced into battle during the first day of an offensive, for completing the breakthrough of the enemy defences. After that the corps swarmed into the operative depth of the enemy defences acting independently of the combined-arms formations and penetrating to depths of from 100-240 km.

After overcoming the tactical zone of defences, the tank and mechanised corps directed their main effort towards a swift penetration into the depth of the enemy defences. The average daily rate of advance by the corps when developing the success was put at 30-35 km, and the maximum reached 60-70 km.

In the meantime the basis for operational and tactical employment of tank forces was reflected in their new organisational structure. To reinforce rifle formations, it was decided to use separate tank brigades and regiments. These were employed as groups, having direct infantry support roles (NPP). Separate regiments, however, equipped with heavy tanks, were intended mainly for combating enemy tanks and self-propelled artillery.

Separate tank brigades usually consisted of three tank and a motorised (rifle) battalions, an artillery battalion, a combat-engineer company, an anti-aircraft battery, and sub-units for combat security and technical supply. There were 65 tanks in a brigade, but there were other variations in tank brigade organisation.

As a rule separate tank regiments consisted of five tank and one mechanised rifle companies, an artillery battery and other combat security and technical supply units.

Following the battle on the Volga, the tank and mechanised corps were used on a wide scale and played an important part in the winter 1942-43 campaigns. In these operations several corps were utilised for developing the operative success along the main direction. The coordination between these corps, however, left much to be desired—principally as the result of a inefficient administrative organisation.

It was in the winter of 1942-43 operations that the tank armies were used. These were massive armoured-tank organisations which were powerful, highly manoeuvrable operative units. Experience with the heterogeneous tank armies showed, however, that such a structure did not allow them to conduct operations of manoeuvre. It had been found that the army commanders could not direct their troops clearly nor could they maintain continuous inter-cooperation between the various formations with their differing mobilities.

In January 1943 the Soviet High Command agreed on the decision to form homogeneous tank armies. Within that year five tank armies of this type were formed, comprised of one to two tank, and one mechanised corps as well as supporting units. From here on, an army establishment included a light artillery brigade, an anti-tank artillery division* and other units. In January 1944 the 6th Tank Army was formed. The fighting establishment of a tank army mounted to 600-700 tanks and SPs, 500-600 guns and mortars, and 30-35,000 men. When attached to a front, tank armies were used as echelons for the development of the success during the offensive, and as a powerful means of inflicting counter-thrusts in defence.

Throughout 1943 the organisational forms of the other types of armoured-tank troops were improved. The combat establishments of the tank and mechanised corps were increased as the result of the inclusion of self-propelled artillery, mortar and anti-aircraft units, liaison sub-units and engineers. The tank corps totalled 207 tanks and 63 SPs, whilst the mechanised had 183 tanks and 63 SPs. They were composed only of medium tanks.

For reinforcing the infantry the Soviets used separate tank brigades, tank and self-propelled artillery regiments and heavy-tank regiments.

At this time the basic type of tank

*It should be mentioned that in the Soviet Army the units 'brigade' and 'division' are reversed. Whereas in the Western armies brigades make up a division, in the Soviet Army divisions make up brigades. The division, in fact, is somewhat analogous in concept to the regiment or battalion.

remained the T-34 medium tank, which was re-armed with the 85 mm gun (T-34-85). Towards the end of 1943 the Soviet tank industry began to turn out the Iosef Stalin heavy tank (IS-2), and production began of several types of self-propelled artillery mounting—the SAU-76,* 85, 100 and the ISU-122, 152.

When using NPP tanks to break through enemy defences the Soviets continued to maintain strict central control in the hands of the rifle division commander. It was only towards the end of 1944, and in 1945, when the number of NPP tanks had increased considerably, that it was possible to parcel out tank units to rifle regiments and battalions.

In general, the coordinated use of tanks in a direct infantry support role, alongside infantry, artillery and engineers, greatly improved. The Field Service Regulations issued during 1943, in which precise directions for the combat employment of tanks in an infantry support (NPP) role were defined, greatly facilitated the improvement of this cooperative action.

In 1943 the Soviets still lacked experience in the use of the new tank armies and most of the army commanders were consulted for their opinions over this. After combining all these opinions, the Soviet High Command decided on the basic method for using tank armies at the start of offensive operations as follows: 'they should be introduced for the breakthrough after the rifle formations have overcome the main defensive zone or all the tactical defensive zones of the enemy.' It was concluded that, following this, a swift operation by the army should be carried out in the operative depth, in cooperation with aircraft and isolated from the main force.

In July 1943 the active army possessed 9,918 tanks and self-propelled guns which then gave it a distinct numerical superiority over that of the Germans.

During the Battle of Kursk all five tank armies took part, as well as 15 separate tank and mechanised corps and many separate tank brigades and regiments. In the defence, separate tank and self-propelled artillery units operated in close cooperation with the infantry and were made organic to the rifle formations. Tank armies and separate tank corps were used for two main roles: firstly, to hold prepared defensive zones either in cooperation with, or independent of, combined-arms armies, and secondly for inserting powerful counter-thrusts. Once the Soviets moved over to the offensive, the armoured-tank troops were used to conduct wide sweeping movements.

Three tank armies (3rd Guards, 2nd and 4th) operated in the Orlovsk direction, in combination with seven separate tank corps. These operations were, however, not very mobile due to the nature of the enemy defences, and the tank armies could not achieve a fast rate of advance. They did, however, provide great force to the advancing fronts by storming numerous defensive positions.

The operations by the two tank armies in the Belgorod-Kharkov direction (5th Guards and 1st), cooperating with seven separate corps, took on a different character. As at the Battle of Stalingrad, the separate corps were used as echelons for the development of the successes by combined-arms armies, and the two tank armies likewise for the Voronezh Front. For the first time the tank armies were used here to break through the tactical zone of defences and then to swiftly develop the offensive. By the fifth day of the offensive they sheered the enemy group and facilitated its subsequent encirclement.

During the final period of the war the quantity of armoured vehicles available increased tremendously. At the beginning of 1944 the active army disposed of 5,357 tanks and SPs. Despite huge losses at Kursk and in the Ukraine, from June 1944 the tank park of the active army was brought up to 7,753 tanks and SPs and, by January 1945, to 12,900 tanks and SPs.

During the initial operations of 1944 the Soviet Army inserted a main thrust

*Sometimes abbreviated to SU.

into the Pravoberezhnoy Ukraine. Here all six tank armies were used together with eight separate tank and mechanised corps and a considerable number of separate tank brigades and regiments. With this mass of troops and equipment they formed powerful 'front mobile groups' which accelerated the achievements of successes.

During 1944 a main thrust was inserted by the Soviet Army in the central sector of the Soviet-German

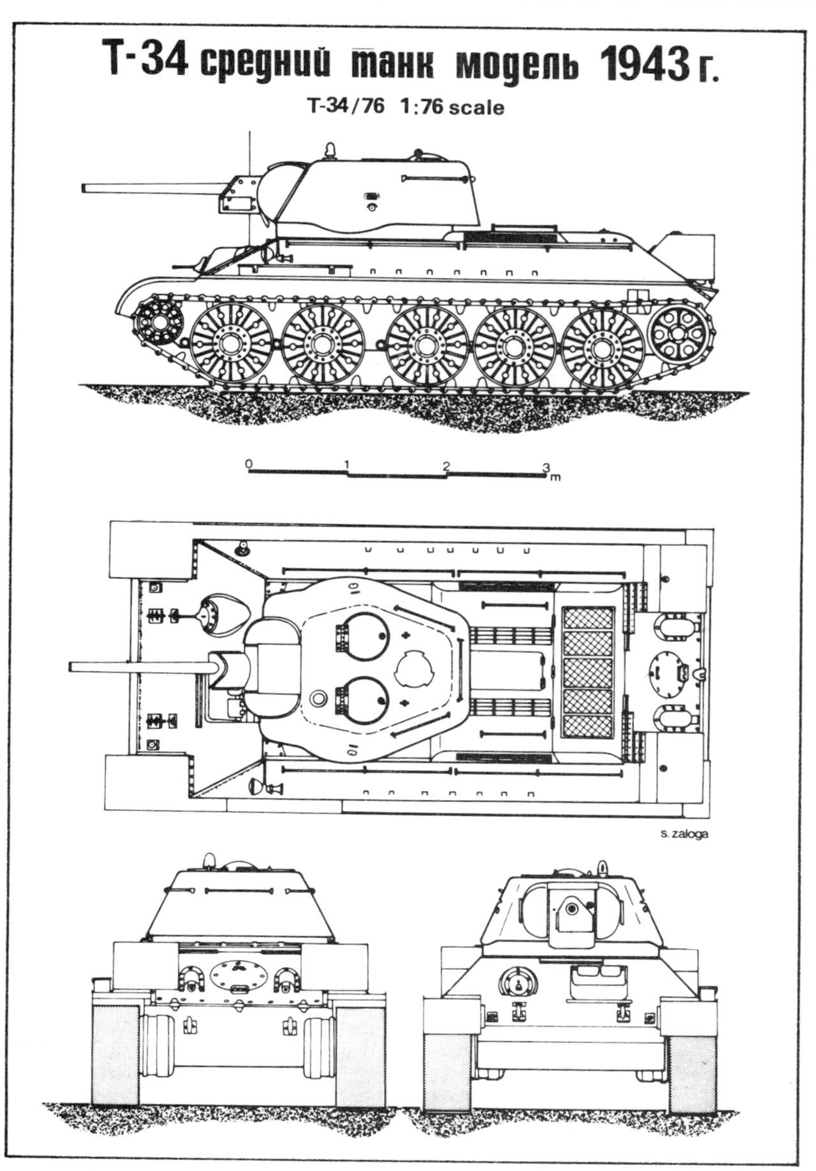

Front—in Belorussia and the Western Ukraine. The basic mass of the armoured-tank troops were used here, comprising five tank armies, ten separate tank and mechanised corps and several scores of separate brigades and regiments. The corps and armies created echelons for the development of the success by armies and fronts respectively. To develop the successes of these fronts, horse-cavalry/mechanised groups were set up. In these operations the offensive was carried to depths from 350-550 km, and they were concluded on the banks of the Visla.

From December 1944 on, guards heavy tank brigades of the Supreme Command Reserve (RVGK) were activated for use in supporting forces when breaking through enemy tactical defence zones. They increased the penetrative capability of advancing forces and the stability of coordinated operations.

The next phase was the thrust from the Visla to the Oder in January 1945. Here the Soviet High Command deployed the largest-ever mass of armoured-tank troops: four tank armies, five separate tank and one mechanised corps (16 corps altogether), six separate tank and two self-propelled artillery brigades, and 23 tank and 41 self-propelled artillery regiments. Altogether, these comprised some 7,500 tanks and SPs. Within 22 days the Soviet troops had moved forward from the Visla to the Oder over a distance of 600 km.

During the subsequent battle for Berlin 6,000 tanks and SPs were massed. On the active sector four tank armies were deployed; two of these (3rd and 4th Guards), after taking Berlin, moved swiftly to Prague where they joined with the 6th Guards Tank Army in the 'liberation' of the city.

The final armoured operation by the Russians in this war was that for the defeat of the Japanese Kwantung Army in Manchuria. The bulk of the units were made organic to the Transbaikal Front which inserted a main thrust across the Great Khingan mountain range into the central region of Manchuria. The 6th Tank Army was deployed in the first operative echelon of the front together with other tank formations. Their appearance in the rear of the Japanese Army made a great contribution to its final defeat. In fact, this was probably the fastest land operation in military history.

two

Soviet tank development

1917-1929

Prior to the Five-Year Plans, little activity took place in the armoured vehicle field apart from tanks. Production of tanks by the Communists began immediately after the October Revolution. Both the Communist Party and the Red High Command correctly appreciated the importance of armoured fighting vehicles and made great efforts to provide the young Red Army with this type of equipment. The whole process was accelerated due to the threat by counter-revolutionary forces and the foreign intervention, and in September 1919 the Higher National Economic Council (VSNCh) formed a special centralised organisation for directing the war industries. This was the Military Industrial Council (SVP). Under the chairmanship of P.A. Bogdanov, president of the VSNCh, a decision was made to begin tank production.

With the urgency of the situation, and due to the lack of experienced automotive and tracked vehicle engineers, it was decided to copy the type of tank which had been captured during the fighting with the Interventionalists. One of the two Renault tanks which had been captured in March 1919 at Odessa, was quickly renovated, and the Military Industrial Council ordered the construction of 15 similar tanks. A special construction group was established under the direction of engineer Khrulev. After two months of intensive effort, this group completed the necessary drawings. This work attracted the personal attention of Lenin. By January 1920 assembly of the first tank was already in progress; the Moscow Car Factory (AMO) supplied the engine, and the armour plate was produced at the Izhorsk Factory in Leningrad. This first tank, called 'Borets za Svobodu tov. Lenin' (Freedom Fighter Comrade Lenin) was released from the factory gates on August 31 1920. Technical trials and the removal of faults occupied the following three months, and on December 1 the Military Industrial Council was able to send Lenin the news of the completion of the first Soviet tank. By the end of 1922 the Krasno Sormovo factory had built 15 such tanks. These tanks were officially designated KS (or Krasno Sormovo), after their factory of origin. Some were armed with a 37 mm gun, others with a machine-gun. Later models had a modified turret mounting both of these weapons.

Subsequently, the Military Industrial Council took steps for the production of further types of tanks. On November 2 1919, the magazine *Izvestia Narodnovo Komissara Po Voyenniem Dielem* (News of the People's Commissariat for Military Activities) published the conditions for a competition sponsored by the council for the best tank design. First prize, totalling 250,000 Roubles, was awarded for a project designated 'Teplokhod AM' (Motor Ship AM), which was submitted by the Izorsk Factory. During 1921 the construction of two such tanks was begun. These tanks were amphibious, weighed about ten tons and were each armed with a 76.2 mm gun mounted in a fully-rotating turret. The crew comprised three men and the power plant was a 90 HP engine mounted transversely. When in water the tank was propelled by a three-bladed propeller.

Dissolution of the Central Command during 1923 interrupted the work on the two original amphibious tanks. At this time the lack of any suitable industrial base and of specialist engineers and designers, coupled with the massive reorganisations taking place in the Red Army, hampered any progress in this field. This difficult situation improved with the formation of the People's

The T-34/76B tank, photographed at Aberdeen Proving Grounds (APG),USA.

Commissariat for Military and Naval Affairs and of the War Industry Main Directorate (GUVP), a division of the Military Industrial Council. On May 6 1924 the GUVP appointed a special Tank Bureau for carrying out the design work and to assist industry in the preparation for the mass-production of tanks. Almost immediately the GUVP began work on a new tank. During May 1925 they designed, amongst others, a prototype heavy tank based on the English Mark V of World War 1. The first design to be brought to the prototype stage was the experimental five-ton infantry support tank T-16. Trials with this vehicle were carried out between June 7 and 15 1927 by a special commission which found the vehicle to be unreliable, and consequently the design was altered, resulting in the T-18 tank which was completed in November. Due to the urgency of providing the Red Army with a modern tank, however, on July 6 1927, the Military Industrial Council officially adopted the tank for service as the MS-1 (Maly Soprovozhdeniya, 1 = Small Accompanying, 1). Serial production of this tank was carried out at the Leningrad Factory 'Bolshevik'. Quantity production began in 1928. By May of that year the Army had been provided with the first 30 of these tanks, and when production ceased in 1931 about 960 of these machines had been turned out. The final versions, extensively modified (improved turrets and suspensions, etc), have been referred to as MS-2 and MS-3 by foreign sources (never officially by the Russians). These tanks weighed between 5.5 and 5.9 tons, and developed each a maximum speed of 16.5 kph. The crew comprised two men. The light weight, small dimensions and compact design of this tank were achieved by transversely mounting the engine in a block integral with the gearbox. The engine developed between 35-40 HP. Armed with a 37 mm gun and one 7.62 mm machine-gun, the tank had 8-16 mm armour. Another novelty was the use of rubber-tyred wheels.

In conformity with the Soviet ideas prevailing in the 1920s over the employment of tanks, in addition to the T-18 type infantry tank, there was a requirement also for a tank able to execute independent roles and to comprise 'manoeuvre groups' working alongside the infantry in greater depth. Such manoeuvre tanks were required to have more powerful armament, thicker armour and greater speed than the T-18. As the result, during the period 1928-29, the design bureau at the Kharkov Locomotive Works designed the new T-12 manoeuvre tank (also referred to as the T-1-12). This tank was submitted for trials early in February 1930. It weighed 19.8 tons,

The T-34/76C (cast turret version), also photographed at APG.

was armed with a 45 mm gun and three machine-guns, and developed 22 kph speed. The crew comprised four men, the armour was 12-22 mm and the engine developed 200 HP. An improved model was the T-24 tank (medium manoeuvre tank), wherein the weight was reduced to 18.5 tons. The T-24 was noted for its three-tier armament arrangement. As before the crew was four men and the armament comprised four 7.62 mm machine-guns. The armour was 8-20 mm and the engine was uprated to 250 HP thereby allowing a maximum speed of 25 kph. Both of these tanks had planetary transmissions which proved to be too complex and difficult to mass produce. Only about 25 T-24s were produced, during 1931, after which production was halted.

1929-1941

During June 1929 a series of lorry and tractor factories were established at Gorky, Moscow, Stalingrad, Chelyabinsk and Yaroslavl. The Ural-Kuznets Basin was developed and the oil industry was begun. The task of technically equipping the Red Army was taken up by the newly-formed organisation headed by the Chief of Armaments for the RKKA, I.P. Uborevits (a post taken over by M.N. Tukhachevsky in 1931).

On July 15 1929 the Red Army General Staff and the leaders of the war industries passed a special directive over the production of tanks and therein approved the 'Minium Programme'. Designers were ordered to direct their attentions towards a wide programme of experimental work. Established by the General Staff was the 'Programme for Armoured-Automobile Supply to the Red Army', which emphasised the need to create mechanised units and to carry out the total mechanisation of the ground forces.

Certain aspects of the programme were related to the developments in foreign armies and led to the formulation of the requirements for tanks and their tactical-technical characteristics. There were a number of problems which had yet to be solved by experimentation and trials, such as the selection of the best types of chassis for tanks, tractors, self-propelled artillery etc. It was required to know the advantages of wheeled, half-tracked, full-tracked, and wheel/tracked chassis.

The programme envisaged also the production of a wide range of armoured vehicles: tankettes for conducting reconnaissance and operating from ambush under the usual conditions of mobile war, small (light) tanks as tools of the mechanised units, medium tanks for breaking through fortified areas during both mobile and positional warfare, large (heavy) tanks for action as tactical battering rams when breaking through strongly fortified enemy positions. It also foresaw the production of SP guns for the support of tank operations, combating enemy tanks and supporting mechanised artillery units, SP AA guns for engaging bomber and ground-attack aircraft (with the dual capability of engaging tanks), SP AA machine-gun mountings for protecting mechanised units, etc. It was also intended to produce command tanks with powerful radio equipment, capable of maintaining communications between armoured-tank and mechanised units, smoke-generating tanks, and completely armoured tracked infantry carriers.

With all these vehicle requirements, all that the Army had at its disposal at that time was the T-18 tank. The General Staff realised that, in order to carry out the programme even in the form of experimental vehicles would be an extraordinarily difficult task and very time-consuming. The programme was to be carried out in the following sequence: light and medium tanks, SP guns, light and medium tractors and armoured carriers. In order that these vehicles (particularly the tanks) could be placed in serial production during 1931-32, their design had to be concluded by autumn 1930. By this time all tests and modifications would have to be completed. With the design experience and facilities then available, however, this could not be achieved.

It was necessary to produce a sufficient quantity of light tanks for group experimentation before embarking on any large-scale production, and at the same time to determine the necessary tactical roles for the new forms of tank units. In other respects, however, as the result of the rapid growth in industry, it was decided in 1929 to organise design bureaux in those factories engaged in tank production, thereby enhancing significantly the progress in research.

There was a shortage of designers and engineers with suitable qualifications and experience. At least the necessary measures could be taken to rectify this situation, and during 1927 young engineers in the autombile factories received special instruction in tank design. As the result, from 1930 onwards, a high-class cadre of specialists appeared who could be used to form a basic design nucleus. The international situation at that time necessitated the rapid carrying out of design

The final model of the KV-1, photographed at APG.

work over the period 1922-1930 and, despite several ambitious and novel innovations, a multiplicity of faults made them unsuitable—particularly from the aspect of large-scale production.

The development of the political situation and the increase in international tension, particularly the threat of war from Japan, necessitated an accelerated rearmament programme. As the result, and due to the impossibility of carrying production of native models on a large scale, the Revolutionary Military Council decided to exploit already well-proven foreign experimental designs and to produce more sophisticated versions at home.

On December 30 1929 a special commission travelled abroad. This was headed by the Director of Mechanisation and Motorisation of the RKKA, I.A. Khalepski, and included the defence industry expert D.F. Budniak. In England this commission purchased samples of Vickers seven and 12-ton tanks, Carden-Loyd tankettes, and other vehicles. In the USA it procured the wheel/track tank designed by Mr W.J. Christie, together with the necessary patents. On the basis of these models Soviet designers elaborated radically modified tanks: the T-27 tankette (for the reconnaissance role), the T-26 light tank as the basic tool for all units of general troop arms and armoured-tank and mechanised units, and the BT fast tank for the large independent armoured-tank and mechanised units.

The T-27 weighed 2.7 tons and had a crew of two men. Due to its small size, the crew usually comprised men of small stature. The armament consisted of a 7.62 mm machine-gun and the armour was 6-10 mm. The maximum speed reached 40 kph.

The T-26 light infantry-support tank was initially twin-turreted. Mass production of this tank began in 1931, after which production was concentrated upon the single-turreted version. The original version weighed eight tons, had a three-man crew, was armed with either one 37 mm gun and a 7.62 mm machine-gun or merely two machine-

The KV-2 heavy tank mounting the 152 mm howitzer. Photographed at the tank museum, Moscow.

guns. (Other armament variations existed.) The armour was 6-13 mm and the 80 HP air-cooled engine gave a vehicle speed of 28 kph.

The BT-2 light wheel/track tank (the BT-1 was purely experimental) was built in several versions. It weighed 10.4 tons and had the same crew, armament and armour as the T-26 gun tank. The 400 HP engine gave a maximum speed of 52 kph on tracks and 72 kph on wheels. When running on wheels (the extreme rear pair were driven) the tracks were carried along the track guards.

On February 13 1931 the Revolutionary Military Council passed a directive accepting these tanks for mass-production. During the final three months of 1931 the Red Army received 17 twin-turreted T-26 tanks (altogether 120 of this version were produced), 348 T-27 tankettes and three BT-2 fast tanks.

At the same time the Soviets demonstrated some of their own designs. One of these was the T-17 tankette prototype (1929), which became known as the 'Lilliput' and was intended to fulfil a variety of roles, such as reconnaissance, liaison, and a chassis for a self-propelled battalion gun. Built specifically for this tank was a 20 HP air-cooled engine and rubber-metal (Kegresse) tracks. The vehicle weighed about 2.4 tons, had a single man crew, was armed with one or two 7.62 mm machine-guns, had 7-14 mm armour, and developed a maximum speed of 16 kph. The T-19 and T-20 light tank prototypes (which became

The T-50 light tank, photographed at the Finnish tank museum. Used only in small numbers before replacement, this particular vehicle has additional armour plates bolted to the turret and front (Steve Zaloga).

important competitors to the T-26) were rejected due to their complexity. The T-23 tankette was a somewhat improved version of the T-17. It was a prototype two-man tankette produced in 1931 as a competitor to the T-27, but the engine was incapable of being mass-produced.

During 1930, in accordance with the plan, new armoured units began to be formed. At the beginning of August 1931 approval was given to build up the armoured-tank and mechanised forces over the period 1931-33. The Council of Labour and Defence was established to carry out the 'Great Tank Programme'. 1932 saw the creation of a large tank industry. Particular emphasis was placed on this by the Government, even at the expense of other types of armaments. About 30 factories began mass producing tanks and other armoured vehicles based on their chassis—SP guns, armoured carriers, etc. Approval was now given for the provision of more diversified tank models; the design bureaux at Kirov and Leningrad worked on designs and prototypes for the light amphibious tanks T-33, T-41 and T-37; the medium tank T-28, and the heavy tank T-35.

The first prototype of the T-33 amphibious tank was produced in 1932. It weighed 3.7 tons, had a two-man crew and was armed with one 7.62 mm machine-gun. The armour was 7.9 mm and the 63 HP engine gave a maximum speed on land of 45 kph. The second prototype had a modified suspension.

The prototype of the T-41 light amphibious tank was produced in 1932. It weighed 3.2 tons, had a two-man crew and was armed with a 7.62 mm machine-gun. The armour comprised 4-9 mm, and the 40 HP engine gave it a speed of 36 kph on land and 4 kph in water.

The first prototype of the T-28 medium tank was released for trials during 1932. It weighed 17.3 tons, had a five-man crew and was armed with one 45 mm gun and three 7.62 mm machine-guns. The armour comprised 20-30 mm and the 500 HP engine provided a maximum speed of 37 kph.

The first prototype of the multi-turreted heavy tank T-35 was built during 1932. It weighed 37 tons, had a nine-man crew, was armed with one 76.2 mm gun, two 37 mm guns and four 7.62 mm machine-guns, and had 20-30 mm armour. The 500 HP engine gave the vehicle a speed of 29 kph.

The Soviets also produced the experimental medium tank series TG as an initial design study for a super-heavy tank weighing 100 tons.

Important work was carried out on engine development. A two-stroke diesel engine developing 400 HP was designed specifically for tank use, and also the BD-2 tank diesel engine which became the prototype for the famous V-2.

It was during this era that the famous tank designer A.A. Morozov began his career, as also L.S. Troyanov, both of whom were later awarded the highest honours for their work on tank design. During the course of the First Five-Year Plan the industrial basis for tank production was established, which enabled rapid progress in the technology of tank production. Over this period industry provided the Red Army with about 3,100 tanks.

On April 19 1932 Marshal Tukhachevsky submitted to the State the progress in the mechanisation and motorisation of the Red Army. During May the Military Academy for Mechanisation and Motorisation was established, which later provided the cadre of armour commanders and technical troops. The production of tanks on a large scale was continued throughout the period of the Second Five-Year Plan. The average yearly output of tanks over the period 1930-31 was 740, during 1932-34 3,371, and during 1935-37 3,139. Thus in the course of six years industry provided the Red Army with about 21,000 tanks.

During the 1930s the BT light wheel/track 'fast' tank became one of the most extensively used and most popular Soviet tanks. The prototype vehicles (models called BT-1 and BT-2) rapidly received commendations and paved the way for further variants. A year after the start of mass production, the new BT-5 model was adopted. It differed from its predecessors mainly with respect to its engine and armament. This model was equipped with a larger cylindrical turret mounting a 45 mm gun co-axial with a machine-gun. In place of the old Liberty engine (which had been built for the BT-1 and 2), this tank used a Soviet aircraft engine adapted for tank use—the Model M5. The tank also had a strengthened chassis. Some (commanders') tanks were fitted with radio equipment, and artillery tanks (designated BT-5A) mounted a 76.2 mm gun co-axial with a machine-gun. This latter version was employed to provide fire

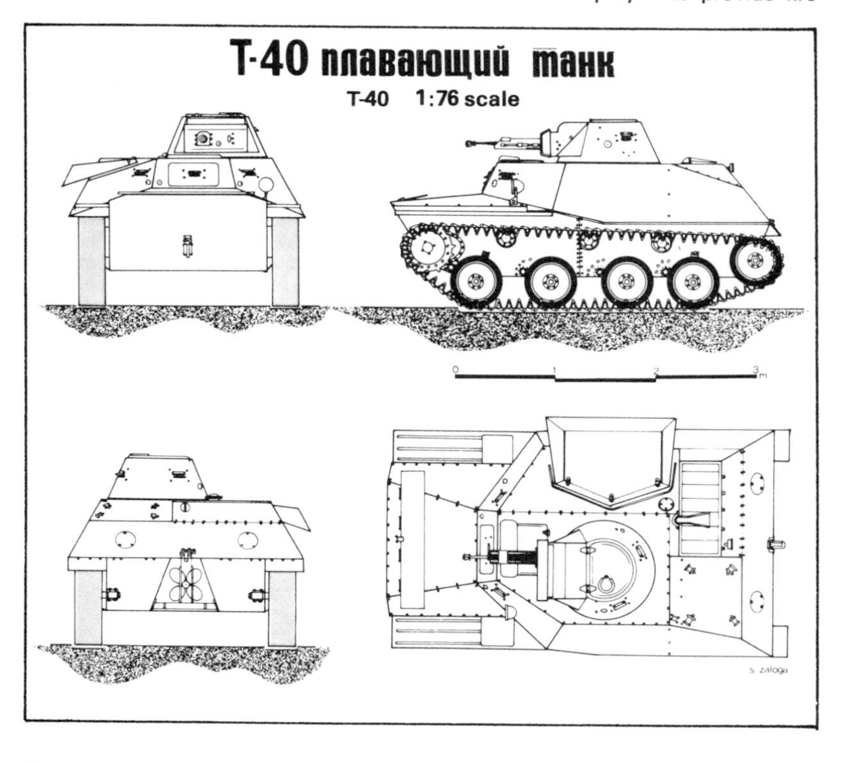

support during attacks by concentrated gun tanks.

During 1935, production began of the successor version, the BT-7, in which several improvements were incorporated. The BT-7-1 (BT-7 Ob.1935) retained the cylindrical turret of the BT-5 tank, but had a new hull which was electro-welded and up-armoured to 15-20 mm. It also had a new M17T engine, improved transmission, increased fuel tank capacity and new smaller-pitched tracks. A later variant produced in 1937, the BT-7-2 (BT-7 Ob.1937) had a new conical type turret.

As with the previous (BT-5) model, an artillery version of the BT-7 was produced designated BT-7A. It mounted a 76.2 mm gun. Due to the increased weight, the facility to move on wheels was removed.

Some BT-7 tanks, in addition to the co-axial machine-gun, had a further machine-gun mounted in the rear of the turret. Other tanks were equipped with an AA machine-gun mounted on top of the turret. From 1938 onwards, these tanks were fitted with the TOS stabilised sight, designed by V.A. Pavlov and A.Z. Tumanov, which considerably improved their ability to fire on the move. About the same time successful trials were carried out with the new V-2 tank diesel engine. As the result of these experiments, in 1939 the Red Army received its first series of diesel-powered tanks, designated the BT-7M (often called the BT-8).

Based on the BT tank, engineers at the Kharkov plant designed a whole range of experimental tanks for various roles. Production of the BT tank was terminated at the end of 1939/beginning of 1940, when the 1940 Tank Programme was introduced.

The T-26 in its original form became the basic type of tank for combined-arms and armoured-tank units. The original model, as mentioned above, had two turrets and varying armament. During 1933 a new model appeared with a single turret (as used on the BT-5 tank), in which was mounted a 45 mm gun and a co-axial machine-gun. Two searchlights were attached to the gun to allow firing by night. The tank was often also equipped with radio (commanders' models), having a characteristic hand-rail type mast circumscribing the upper part of the turret. The tank's weight now rose to 9.4 tons, which caused excessive increase in the ground pressure. During the following year a small number of artillery support tanks (called Artillery Tank T-26) were produced, mounting 76.2 mm guns. Experience showed, however, that such a tank was incapable of mounting this armament due to the limitations on crew space. The low speed and mobility of theT-26 in comparison with the BT initiated work on a new replacement light tank and, simultaneously, during the mid-1930s, caused a discontinuation in production.

The replacement tank was the T-46. This resembled the T-26 externally, but had a chassis similar to that of the BT. When running on wheels, all the axles were driven, which greatly complicated

The T-70 light tank, final light tank model to be mass-produced by the Soviets during World War 2.

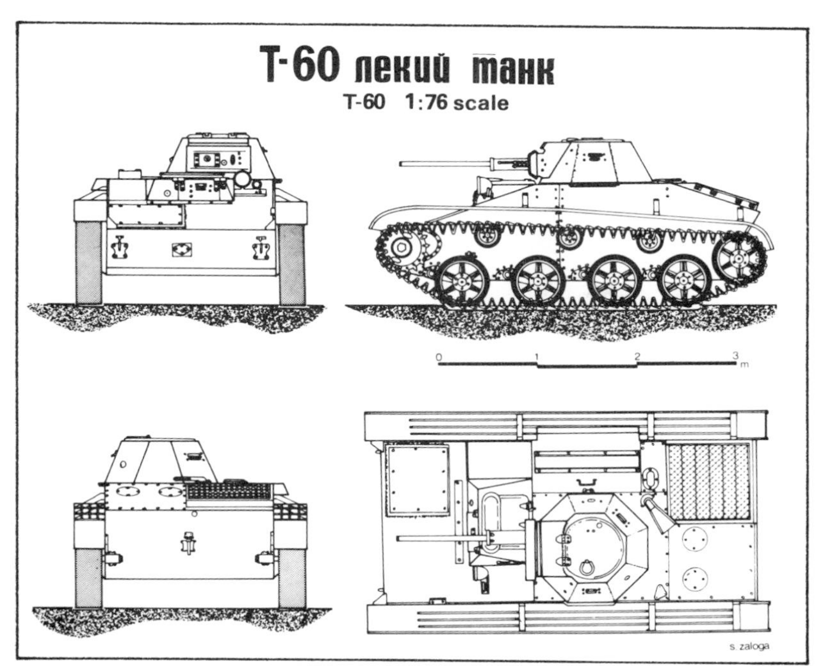

the overall layout of the tank. After production of a small series of this vehicle, therefore, a new variant of the T-26 was adopted.

From 1937 the T-26 received a new conical turret having improved ballistic shape (similar to that of the BT-7-2). Somewhat later, the hull armour was redesigned to provide sloping side plates and was now welded as opposed to riveted. This new model received the designation T-26S. Some of these tanks were provided with an additional machine-gun in the rear of the turret, and others an additional AA machine-gun served by the tank commander. As with the later models of the BT tank, the very latest T-26 vehicles received a stabilised sight. From 1932 onwards the T-26 chassis became used as the basis for various types of SP weapons, armoured carriers and specialised tanks. Flame-throwing versions were adopted as standard (including the OT-26, OT-130 and OT-133).

In the tankette and light reconnaissance tank class, during the mid-1930s the light two-man amphibious tanks T-37 and T-37A were adopted following a long series of prototypes. In the production of these maximum use was made of automobile components. An interesting feature of these tanks was that the water-propulsion screw had a variable pitch allowing simple reverse drive when afloat. The T-37A was produced up until 1936, after which it was replaced by new models in this class, the T-38 and the T-38M series, which had comparable performance but were of greatly improved design. In the period following the introduction of these models several experimental types were built, giving rise in 1940 to the T-40 amphibious tank.

After trials with early prototypes in the medium tank class (T-12, T-24, TG), which for many reasons proved unsuitable for mass production, in 1932, at the Kirov plant in Leningrad, a special prototype medium tank was designed—the T-28. This was intended to amplify the tactical performance of infantry and cavalry units as a means of breaking through strongly fortified defensive positions. As mentioned

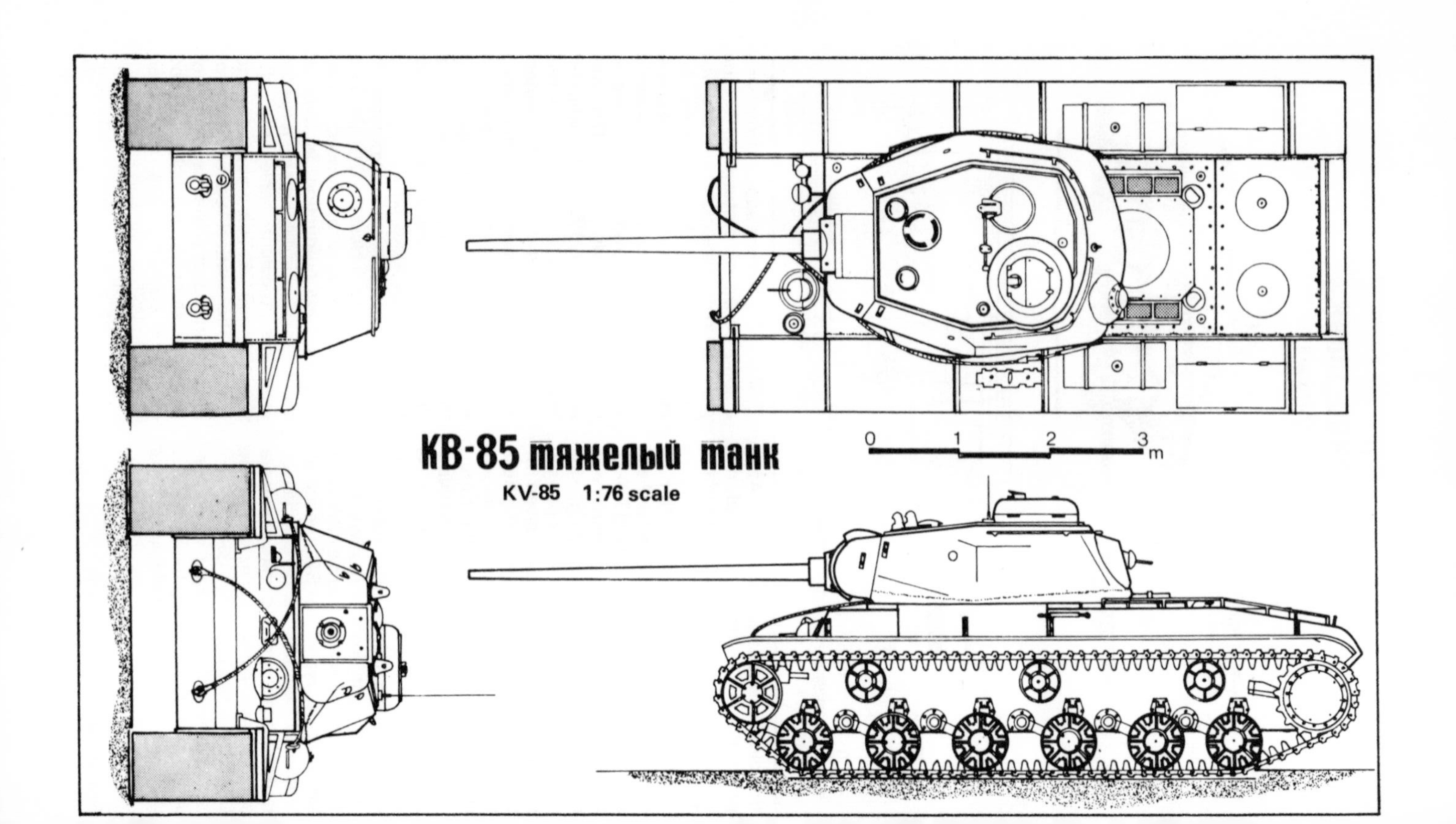
КВ-85 тяжелый танк
KV-85 1:76 scale
0
1
2
3
m

above, the first prototype of this three-turreted tank was armed with a 45 mm gun in the main turret and one machine-gun in each of the subsidiary one-man turrets. The production version was further developed, as the result of which the weight increased to 28 tons and the 45 mm gun was replaced by a 76.2 mm weapon of 16.5 calibres length. A further machine-gun was mounted in the main turret. All vehicles were fitted with radio equipment and apparatus for laying smoke screens. In later production models a device was used to stabilise the main turret. Later, during 1938, this tank was subjected to extreme modernisation. The existing gun was replaced by the Model L-10 of 26 calibres barrel length. T-28 tanks were first used operationally during September and October 1939 and then during the initial battles in Finland during the winter of 1939-40. (This is according to official Soviet statements, although there is strong evidence to suggest that the tank was used in Spain in 1936-37.) During the course of the Finnish war it was shown that the armour on the T-28 was too thin and steps were taken to rectify this. Special armoured screens were fitted, and the turret and hull frontal plates were increased from 50 to 80 mm. The sides and rear received 40 mm armour. As the result, the weight of this tank rose to 32 tons. This up-armoured tank has been referred to as the T-28M and proved itself when breaking through the Mannerheim Line in 1940.

Somewhat earlier, however, a decision had been made to design a new type of tank which would be much faster than the previous vehicles. It had been found that the T-28 had developed insufficient speed and that the tracks wore out too easily, thereby limiting the range of operation. As the result, the successor type of medium tank was to be a wheel/track vehicle on the lines of the BT tank.

During 1934, in the design bureau at the Kirov factory in Leningrad, the engineers elaborated a wheel/track variant of the T-28 tank, designated Medium Tank T 29-5. The young engineer M.I. Koshkin, who later led the design of the famous T-34 tank, participated in the design of this vehicle. As regards armament and armour, the T 29-5 tank did not differ radically from the T-28. It did have, however, a new chassis of the wheel/track type. All axles were driven directly through multiple transmissions. This considerably enhanced the vehicle's performance across country, which could now be achieved even on wheels. A year later a further variant was produced, the T 29, which could achieve the same speeds on wheels as on tracks. This was obtained through the use of a special synchromesh transmission system. As the result of their complex design, however, neither tank progressed beyond the experimental stage.

During 1936 Koshkin was reassigned to the 'Komintern' factory in Kharkov, in the post of chief designer. Considering his age this was quite remarkable, but he soon proved the soundness of this decision. At the design bureau of this factory, which at that time was concentrating upon the production of the BT tank, extensive work was being carried out on the improvement of this tank. Personnel working on the BT-5 model had adapted it to take the new BD-2 diesel engine, which was later developed into the V-2 diesel.

Further development of Soviet tanks resulted from astute observations on the part of the Soviet High Command over the Civil War in Spain. It is not known who was actually responsible, for the Soviets have never mentioned any names in this respect. This latter fact makes it almost certain that these observations were expounded by one of the brilliant exponents of tank warfare 'liquidated' during the period 1937-1941—namely D.G. Pavlov or Marshal M.N. Tukhachevsky. The observations were in connection with the increased effectiveness and the quantity of contemporary anti-tank weapons. It appeared that the type of tank then in use lost its lead over the other arms through a gradual reduction in armour effectiveness. For this reason it was decided in the Soviet Union to carry out work on so-called 'shell-proof tanks'—ie tanks whose armour protected them not only from small-arms fire and shell splinters, but also from direct hits by small-calibre artillery weapons. In order to reduce the effect upon tanks of this type of weapon, orders were given to begin experimentation on new tank projects with considerably greater armour and more powerful armament.

At the beginning of 1937 the Kharkov factory was assigned the task of designing a new tank, a wheel/track design with the factory designation of A20. The design of this tank was commenced during November of that year. The A20 had a new shaped hull made up of steeply inclined welded plates. The chassis was similar to that employed on the BT tank, but power was transmitted to three pairs of wheels. At the same time a further version, armed with a 76.2 mm gun, was developed and designated A30.

The complex technology associated with enabling both wheel and track drive, however, considerably increased the weights of the tanks and, furthermore, caused difficulties in mass production and maintenance. For this reason Koshkin, working in conjunction with his assistant A.A. Morozov, proposed the design of a further variant, the T-32, which was purely tracked. Thanks to not having to cater for moving on wheels, in this vehicle it was possible to increase the armour basis without fear of violating the weight limit imposed by tactical and technological stipulations. On being presented this new tank project, during a meeting in August 1938, the Main Military Council of the USSR accepted it and sanctioned the construction of a prototype.

Prototypes of both the A30 and the T-32 tanks (the latter at that time being called the A32) were completed at Kharkov at the beginning of 1939, and during that year were demonstrated to the Armoured Commission. Both tanks were subjected to extensive technical and tactical trials, which showed them to be extremely versatile vehicles. The Commission recommended an increase in the armour basis on the T-32 and the application of more powerful armament. So modified, the successor variant was exhibited by the group under Koshkin as the Project T-34.

At the time when this project was presented it was yet uncompleted, so that the decision as to which tank to adopt rested on the analysis of the military situation developing during that early stage of World War 2. On December 19 1939 the Stavka accepted the T-34 for adoption by the armoured-tank and mechanised units of the Red Army—without even awaiting the completion of a prototype vehicle.

At the Komintern factory, towards the end of January 1940, the first production models of the T-34 were completed. At the beginning of February two of these tanks, under the personal direction of Koshkin, conducted a trial march circumscribing Kharkov—Moscow—Smolensk—Kiev—Kharkov. In Moscow the tank was presented before the High Command. During June the drawings were completed and this tank entered mass production. Whilst conducting the trial march, Koshkin contracted pneumonia and was rushed to hospital where he died on September 26 1940. Being probably the greatest tank designer of our time this was a great shame and one can only speculate as to the eventual effect his continued work might have had on armour both in World War 2 and today.

Despite many minor faults, it might be argued that the T-34 was the first *real* tank, in the modern interpretation of the word. In this vehicle—for the very first time—had been achieved an almost perfect balance between firepower, mobility and armour protection. In all other tank designs up until that time one or two of these factors had always been given some level of emphasis to the detriment of the other(s). The design of the T-34 was to set the trend for all future tank development throughout the world, indeed up until this very moment. Apart from the fact that the tank gave the Russians a technological lead over their contemporaries, particularly the enemy, another remarkable feature was its tremendous potential for increases in both armour and armament, which allowed this model to remain the standard medium tank of the Soviet Army right up to the mid-1950s. This was indeed an unprecedented achievement, particularly when one considers the continual redesign which took place in all other countries throughout World War 2 and the early post-war period.

When it first appeared, the T-34 was noted for its excellently-shaped turret and hull armour, its powerful 76.2 mm gun, and its remarkable suspension, running gear and diesel engine. The use of the V-2 diesel engine reduced the fire risk and substantially increased the range of operation of this tank in comparison with those powered by conventional ICE engines. The independent suspension, a development of the Christie-type used on the BT tank, permitted high speed even on rough terrain, whilst the wide tracks enabled the vehicle to traverse mud and snow. The overall design of the tank facilitated rapid mass production as well as the expedient execution of field repairs and maintenance.

Since production of the T-34 began only in June 1940, by the end of that year only 115 of these tanks were completed. During the following year production was greatly increased, now being shared by other factories, and by the outbreak of the war (June 22 1941) 1,110 had been produced during 1941.

The tank was originally equipped (Model Ob.1940) with the 76.2 mm L-11 Model 1939 gun mounted in a welded turret of rolled plate. In order to accelerate production, however, a new turret was specially designed (by Morozov) which could be cast. During mid-1941 the new F34 Model 40 tank gun was adopted which had a longer barrel.

Whilst great steps were being taken in the development of the medium tank, similar remarkable achievements were being made in the heavy tank field.

The first prototype of the multi-turreted T-35 heavy tank, a vehicle intended for executing similar tasks to the T-28 and forming the tool of independent heavy tank brigades at the disposal of the Supreme Command Reserve, was designed during 1932. The characteristic feature of this relatively large tank was its multiplicity of armament: a 76.2 mm gun in the main turret and smaller calibre guns and machine-guns in separate auxiliary turrets. Altogether, the armament was located in five separate turrets. The first variant of this tank weighed 37 tons and

The final KV model, produced as a stop-gap pending the arrival of the IS heavy tank—the KV-85.

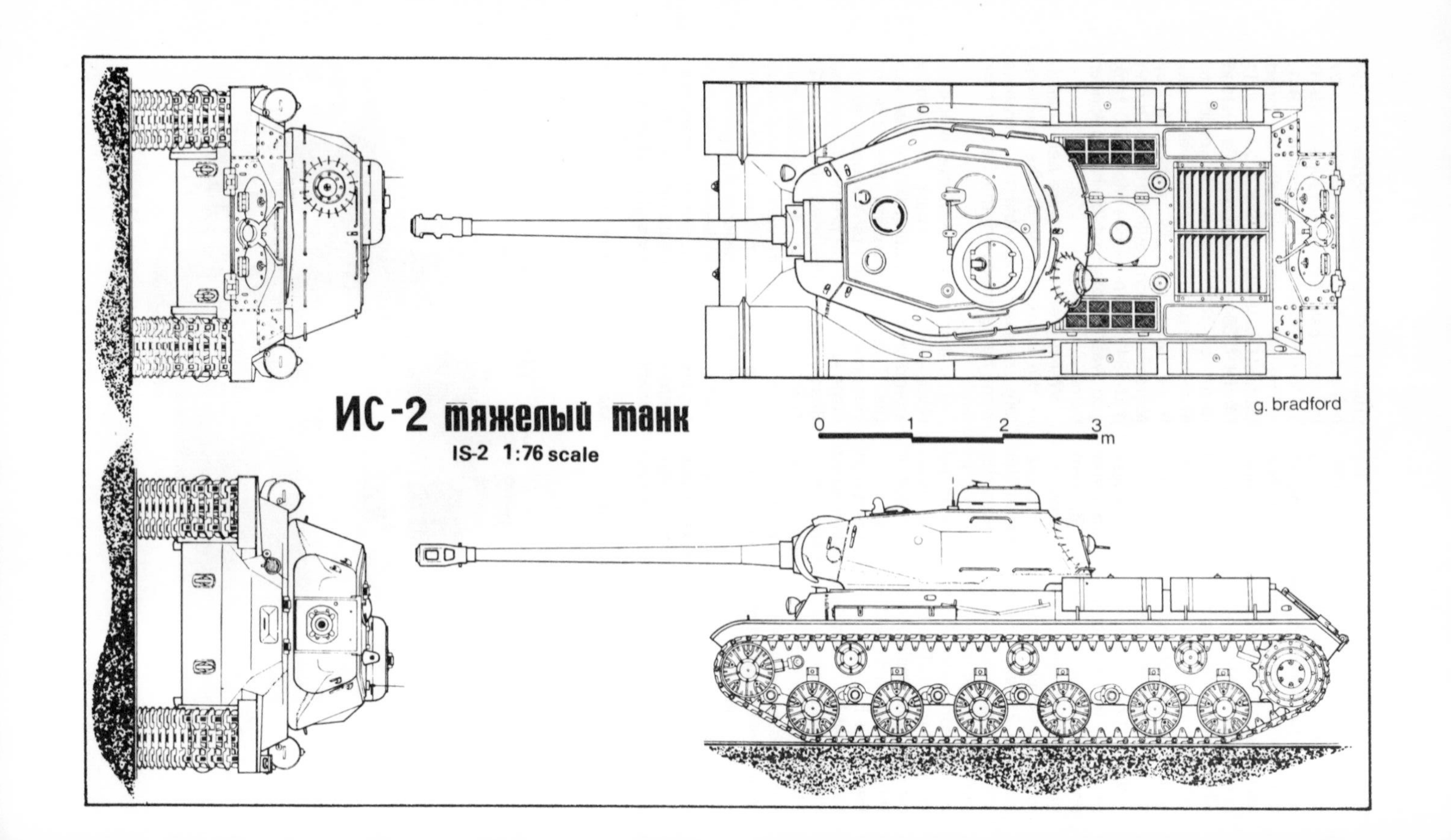
g. bradford
0
1
2
3
m
ИС-2 тяжелый танк
IS-2 1:76 scale

had 20-30 mm armour. Apart from the 76.2 mm gun in the main turret it had two 37 mm guns and four machine-guns. The chassis had six pairs of road wheels grouped in twin bogies. The second version had a lengthened chassis (eight wheels per side) and 45 mm guns in place of the 37 mm ones. In this case the weight rose to 45 tons. This latter model served the troops during the period 1935-36.

Two years later a final version of the tank was designed having fewer auxiliary turrets. Up until 1939, when production ceased, only a small series were turned out. The majority of these tanks were used at the beginning of the war but were rapidly destroyed by the Germans.

As the result of the demands made for the utilisation of 'shell-proof armour', work on a new heavy tank was undertaken directly by the design bureau at the Kirov factory in Leningrad, which had already designed the T-28 medium and the T-35 heavy tanks earlier.

One of the first models of a tank with shell-proof armour was designed in the spring of 1937. This was the T-46—T-46-5 series, which later received the designation T-111. The most important feature of these tanks was the 60 mm armour basis, which guaranteed adequate protection from hits by 37 mm shot at all ranges and 76 mm shot at ranges above 1,200 m. Apart from the thick armour the tank was rather conventional and served only to provide experience in mastering the production of exceptionally thick armour.

Subsequently, the group under the direction of Kotin designed preliminary variants of two heavy tanks—SMK (Sergius Mironovits Kirov) and T-100 (Sotka), wherein components of the T-35 and T-111 tanks were utilised. These tanks were little more than much more heavily armoured versions of the T-35. At this stage the designers were ordered to reduce the number of turrets to two. Whilst carrying out this the designers once more received instructions (from Stalin personally) to design a further model simultaneously, now having only one turret. During 1939 the first prototypes of the twin-turreted tanks SMK and T-100 were completed. Both models had armour up to 60 mm thick and were powered by petrol engines. In the SMK tank use was made of independent torsion-bar suspension. The chassis of the T-100 was later used as a basis for the heavy SU-100U SP.

Work on the single-turreted prototype, which received the designation KV (Kliment Voroshilov), was undertaken at the Kirov Factory during February 1939. By the beginning of September this model had already undergone extensive factory trials, after which it was demonstrated to members of the Main Military Council. A directive dated December 19 passed the tank as suitable for serial production.

In the meantime, during the early days of December, the Russo-Finnish War had broken out. During the offensive on the Mannerheim Line, which commenced on December 17, six SMK and KV tanks were tried out. On February 11 1940 they participated in the battle on the Karelian Isthmus during the breakthrough of the second zone of defences at Summa. The new tanks were used to support infantry directly when breaking through fortified defences. Despite the tremendous firepower of the Finnish defences, the thick armour adequately protected these tanks from serious damage. During the entire period of battle only two tanks out of the six were immobilised—and these were of the multi-turreted type. The KV proved well its special features. Its 75 mm armour withstood rounds from all types of anti-tank guns and the armament, the 76.2 mm L11 or F32 gun of 30.5 calibres barrel length and machine-guns, provided immense firepower. Other qualities of the tank were the reliability of the diesel engine, the independent suspension on all wheels using internally anchored torsion bars, and the wide tracks providing low ground pressure. The new heavy tank could develop relatively high speed, achieve a large radius of action and had a great capacity for surmounting artificial and natural obstacles. At the same time, simplicity of design facilitated rapid mass-production and simplified field maintenance and repairs. This first model of the KV tank was designated KV-1.

In February 1940 a second version was produced, the KV-2. This vehicle, officially classed as an 'artillery tank', was designed to provide supporting fire to armoured and mechanised units during breaks-through of strongly fortified defensive positions. It had a large, heavy turret, in which was originally mounted a 122 mm howitzer (first production run), but later it was equipped with a 152 mm howitzer. Due to the increased weight, 52 tons, the KV-2 had a noticeably reduced speed and a limited radius of action. Firing could be conducted only from a static position, and the overloading of the tank through the massive turret greatly deteriorated the vehicle's cross-country performance. For these reasons the KV-2 variants were eventually replaced by armoured SPs in which the same weapons were mounted directly in the hull.

Towards the end of 1940—beginning of 1941, the KV-1 tank was re-armed with the ZIS-5 gun of 41.6 calibres barrel length and somewhat increased effective range. On the eve of the war KV tanks were produced with the armour increased in places to 110 mm. Some vehicles were fitted with appliqué armour, others had screens fastened by characteristic bolts (mainly on the turret, and hull front). About the same time the armour foundries in the Kuznets Basin produced a slightly modified turret which was entirely cast. The production of this turret, which weighed over seven tons and had a frontal thickness of 100-120 mm, was quite a feat of engineering.

Mass production of the KV tank began at the beginning of 1940. By the end of that year the Red Army had received 243 of these tanks, and by June 1941 a further 393.

Concurrently with the production of new medium and heavy tanks, the 1940 Tank Programme foresaw the requirements for a new light tank and a new light amphibious tank. As before, an attempt was made to provide the light tank with shell-proof armour, the result being the T-50. In the case of the amphibious light tank, however, buoyancy limitations forbade this and the resulting vehicle, the T-40, was rather conventional in its design—although welding replaced riveting in its construction.

The T-50 light tank was designed as a replacement for the T-26 and BT tanks, being intended to support infantry and to carry out reconnaissance missions. Like the T-34 it was characterised by its greatly inclined armour on the hull and turret. The armour was of equal thickness throughout, which is unusual in tank design. Mounting a 45 mm gun, the vehicle could achieve a speed of 60 kph. The tank had torsion bar

An IS-1 heavy tank approaching Berlin. This particular vehicle has a hybrid muzzle-brake.

The last of the line. The IS-3 heavy tank taking part during the victory parade in Berlin 1945. Undoubtedly the most powerful tank right up until the end of the 1950s.

suspension and, due to its similarity in construction to the KV tank, was often referred to as the 'Mali Klim' (Little Klim). A special diesel engine was used to propel this vehicle. Since this complex tank required as much production effort as the T-34 medium, however, production was discontinued after only 65 vehicles had been delivered.

The T-40 was a replacement for the Soviet amphibious light tank series (T-37, 37A and T-38). It was introduced to equip reconnaissance units and armoured liaison units at the beginning of 1941. Its armament comprised machine-guns only (one 12.7 mm and one 7.62 mm) and the armour was relatively thin. To reduce cost and production time it utilised various autombile components, particularly in the engine and transmission. In accordance with the new design generation it had fully independent suspension. Since the thin armour proved to be ineffective a further series employed thicker armour but, due to the increase in weight, the water-propulsion system was removed making the tank now purely a land vehicle. Immediately prior to the outbreak of the war T-38 amphibious tanks in service were retrofitted with 20 mm aircraft cannon.

1941-1945

The development of Soviet armour during the period of the Russo-German conflict was not so diverse as in other countries—purely because the Soviet tanks were so much more advanced than any others. The Soviets 'called the tune', and as the Germans developed model after model, all the Soviets needed to do was to introduce some counter-modification to their two basic tanks—the T-34 and the KV. It was only towards the end of the war that the Russians introduced a new tank—the IS (Iosef Stalin), but even this was only a redesigned KV and not an entirely new design. For this reason an evolutionary account of Soviet tank development during the war is by no means as lengthy as for previous eras.

Soon after the start of the conflict T-34s and KVs received extensive modifications resulting from experience gained at the fronts. Industry also made several redesigns to enable more rapid and efficient production of the vehicles. Some of the modifications introduced were: new track links with special grousers, new resilient road wheels, improved turrets (usually cast), gun mantlets, drivers' hatches, louvres, cupolas, hull machine-gun mountings, and improved transmissions and final

The SU-76, 76.2 mm self-propelled gun based on the T-70 light tank. Photographed at APG.

drives. All tanks were eventually fitted with two-way radio equipment.

In order to increase the tanks' protection from the new types of armour-piercing ammunition, additional armoured screens or appliqué armour were attached to the hull and turret fronts.

Despite the stagnancy in medium and heavy tank development, there was considerable activity in the light tank field. Following the unsuccessful T-50, the Soviets produced the T-60 light tank. Still utilising automobile components, it had thicker armour and more powerful armament than the T-40.

At the beginning of 1942 a new T-34 model was produced. In place of the original turret a new hexagonal one was used which lent itself better to mass production. To simplify the production of hulls a new system of automatic welding was introduced. The fuel capacity was increased, and the tank was equipped with additional exterior fuel tanks which increased the range of operation considerably. During the winter of 1942-43 this tank received a commander's cupola. A five-speed gearbox was also introduced together with a new clutch.

Towards the end of 1942 the chassis of the T-34 tank was used to build one of the first Soviet Army SPs—the SU-122. Mass-production of this vehicle began in December 1942.

During 1943 a small number of T-34 tanks were produced with much thicker armour, and designated T-43. This tank was not very successful since the increase in weight reduced its performance.

Operational experience with the KV tank which, as the result of successive modifications, got heavier and heavier, demanded a reduction in weight. Modification of the tank was undertaken during the summer of 1942. In order to increase the speed and mobility of the tank the armour thickness was reduced to a 75 mm basis on the front and 60 mm on the sides. As the result the weight dropped to 42.5 tons. The tank had other important modifications, principally in the transmission. The engine cooling system was also improved as well as the lubrication system. So modified, the tank was designated KV-1s (skorotniy = fast). Mass-production of this model commenced during August 1942.

About the same time the Gorky Automobile Plant began producing a new light tank, the T-70. Once again this tank employed existing lorry components. It was soon realised, however, that a two-man crew was inadequate and production was stopped—although by that time 8,226 had been produced. A modification to the T-70 chassis enabled it to be used as the basis for the SU-76 self-propelled 76 mm gun. Eventually the role of the light tank was taken over completely by the medium T-34.

Following analysis of the battles and campaigns of the second half of 1942, the Soviet High Command demanded a means of providing attacking tanks with powerful artillery support. Conventional artillery was incapable of achieving this due to its poor mobility, low speed and lack of protection. For this reason the Commissariat for Defence ordered the design of prototype SP guns based on tank chassis.

With the appearance of the new German Tiger heavy tank and various self-propelled guns, it became necessary to provide a gun of greater range which could pierce their armour. This was achieved through the adoption of the 85 mm anti-aircraft gun for tank use. At the end of summer 1943 a heavy cast turret was fitted to the chassis of the KV-1s mounting the 85 mm gun. (This turret had already been designed for the projected IS-1 heavy tank, then still in the experimental stage). The resulting tank was designated KV-85 and it remained in production until the end of the autumn as a stop-gap pending the introduction of the 'Stalin.'

During the autumn of 1943 a turret of similar design to that fitted to the KV-85 was attached to the T-34 tank. This mounted the 85 mm ZIS S-53 or D-5T gun. The new tank, called the T-34-85, had thicker turret armour. The slight increase in tank weight, however, did not adversely affect its mobility. The 85 mm gun could penetrate the frontal hull armour of the Tiger at 1,000 m using arrowhead shot (sub-calibre), although the accuracy was not all that good.

About the same time an 85 mm SP version of the T-34 was introduced, designated SU-85.

In anticipation of further German progress in heavy tanks, the Commissariat of Defence ordered the design of a more heavily armoured heavy tank than the KV, mounting more powerful armament. Towards the end of 1943 21 prototypes of tanks and SPs were produced, six of which were accepted for mass production. Most important of these was the Iosef Stalin (IS) tank—designed by the group of engineers under Kotin. Through clever armour application and improved automotive layout Kotin achieve the most effective design of heavy tank for minimum weight. Although classed as a heavy tank by the Soviets, the vehicle in fact weighed almost the same as the German Panther medium tank. The initial series mounted the KV-85 turret, but soon the 122 mm gun was adopted, firing separate ammunition. Although the large calibre gun reduced the ammunition stowage and rate of fire, it allowed Soviet heavy tank crews to engage enemy tanks at extremely long ranges and certainly engage any type of tank which the Germans could field at that time.

Production of IS tanks was begun at the end of 1943, when 102 were built, and during the following year 2,250 were turned out. They were used to equip independent heavy tank regiments of the Supreme Command Reserve. The IS-2 model received an improved hull with contoured castings. On these tank chassis the Soviets developed the heavy SPs—ISU-122 and ISU-152.

During the final stages of the war, Kotin personally observed the battles in which the IS tanks were engaged, and as the result was able to gain valuable operational experience. Subsequently, he produced the IS-3 tank which entered service just in time to take part in the Victory Parade in Berlin during 1945. The basic alteration was to the distribution of armour. Thicker plates were used on the hull, sloped at greater angles, and a carapace (maximum strength) shaped turret was utilised.

Apart from numerous experimental models, this concludes the technological development of Soviet armour up until the end of World War 2.

three

Soviet tank camouflage and markings

The Soviet Army never adopted a comprehensive set of rules governing tank markings. Most tanks went into action without any markings whatsoever, and those markings which did exist were often of a local, improvised nature. On the whole, the frequency of markings increased after 1943 since the more widespread use of radios necessitated call numbers and the like.

Vehicle colouring

Soviet tanks were uniformly finished in a very dark green at the factory; camouflage, aside from the use of white and light grey in winter months, was extremely uncommon. The shade of the dark green varied from factory to factory. On those KV-1s and T-34s supplied to the US and Britain for trials in 1942, the colour was a very dark black green, equivalent to US FS 24052.

National insignia

The red star, though popular on pre-war parade vehicles, was hardly ever seen on Russian tanks again until 1944-45 when its use increased modestly. In the final year of the war, it was possible to see it painted in both white and red.

Patriotic slogans

The use of bold patriotic slogans was a unique feature of Soviet markings during the war, though modellers have tended to exaggerate their importance and frequency of use. Several distinct categories of these slogans can be distinguished. The 'true' patriotic slogan, such as 'Za Rodinu!' (For the Motherland!) was popular throughout the war. By 1942 'battle' slogans had appeared such as 'Frontu na Razgrom Fashizma!' (To the front for the rout of

Specific unit symbols (not to constant scale). **1** *Insignia of 64th Guards Tank Brigade. The insignia of the 41st Guards Tank Brigade was the same minus the box.* **2** *Sign of the 366th Guards Heavy Self-propelled Artillery Regiment.* **3** *Sign of the 3rd Tank Brigade, 1st Battalion. (Battalion designated by inset number.)* **4** *135th Tank Brigade, 2nd Battalion.* **5** *39th Tank Brigade, 3rd Battalion.* **6** *Insignia possibly of 16th Mechanised Army.* **7** *Insignia possibly of 3rd Guards Tank Army.* **8** *Insignia possibly of 5th Tank Army.* **9** *Insignia of 63rd Chelyabinsk Tank Brigade.* **10** *Insignia of Guards 78th Heavy Tank Regiment.* **11** *Insignia of 1443rd Self-propelled Artillery Regiment.* **12-15** *Units unknown.*

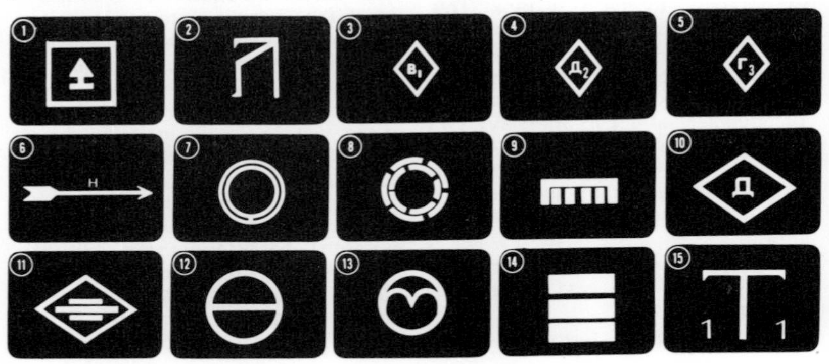

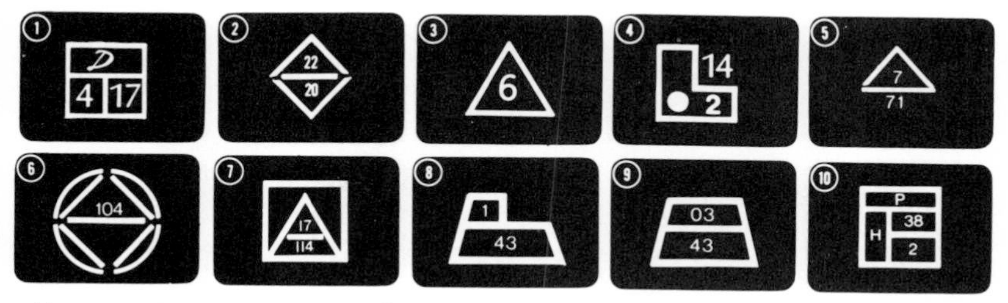

Non-specific unit symbols. **1** *1202nd Self-propelled Artillery Regiment, 4th Battery, 17th vehicle.* **2-10** *Units unidentified.*

fascism!) or 'Smert nyemyetzkim fashistam!' (Death to the German fascists!). Names recalling past heroes of Russian or Soviet history were used: Suvorov, Shchortz, etc, as well as the names of heroes of the existing war. This style was one of the least common. Finally, late in the war, slogans with a distinctly political tinge began to appear such as '20 Years of Soviet Rule in Uzbekistan' or 'For Soviet Estonia', etc, and often these slogans were in one of the languages other than Russian. One of the most common sort of 'slogan', which was in fact not a slogan at all, was the dedication marking. As in Britain and the US, unions, collectives and so on pooled their donations and 'purchased' vehicles for the troops. Often this amounted to the purchase of a whole company of tanks, and all of the tanks in the unit were emblazoned with the name of the group, such as 'Moscow Collective Farm'.

Tactical markings

Soviet tactical markings, consisting of symbols and numbers, were usually, painted in white and almost invariably were confined to the turret area. The use of turret numbers increased in frequency in direct proportion to the use of inter-vehicle radios and was most common after 1943. Numbers were most often used in two and three digit combinations and could also be seen in conjunction with cyrillic letters. There was never a comprehensive system for turret numbering, and this was left to the discretion of local officers.

KV-1 with the patriotic slogan 'We defend the conquests of October' in white on the turret sides.

A T-70 light tank in winter whitewash with the number 343 and the slogan 'Moscow' in red on the turret sides (National Archives).

Slogans. **1** *Death to the German Fascists!* **2** *For the Soviet Ukraine (in Ukrainian).* **3** *Onward to the West.* **4** *To the front for the rout of fascism.* **5** *Onward to Riga.* **6** *We defend the conquests of October (referring to the 1917 Revolution).* **7** *Chelyabinsk Collective Farmers.* **8** *Khabarovski Youth Group.* **9** *Suvorov (18th Century Russian General).* **10** *Shchortz (general in the Civil War).*

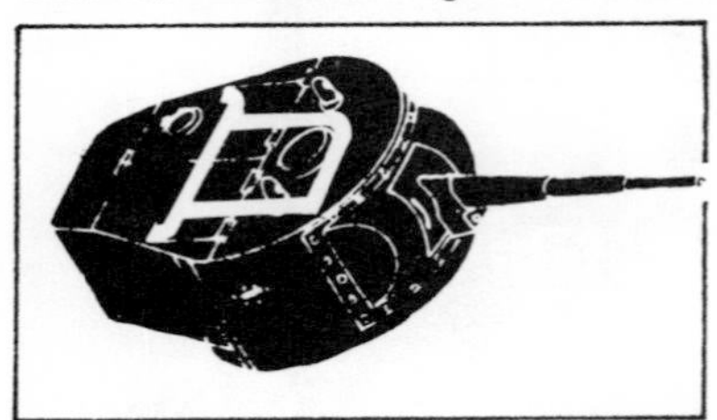

T-26 with typical pre-war air identification marking—a large white cyrillic letter 'D'.

T-34, circa 1943, showing a typical air identification band of the period.

Tactical symbols can be roughly lumped into two groups, non-specific symbols and specific symbols. Non-specific symbols consisted of a geometric stencil, not specific in shape to the given unit, into which was added numbers which distinguished the regiment and individual vehicle. To give an example, the bisected diamond was used by dozens of units but was not peculiar to one in particular. This type of insignia was used throughout the war, and generally was not accompanied by turret numbers (though there are many exceptions). Specific symbols differed from the earlier style in that the shape of the symbol was often specific to only one single unit, and secondly, the symbol only designated the higher formation (brigade, regiment, etc) and did not contain any information about the individual vehicle's number. This later characteristic meant that this type of symbol was usually supplemented by a turret number which contained the other information.

T-34/76, circa 1944, displaying a red star edged in white, and a three-digit call number preceded by a cyrillic 'L'.

A T-34/76 with the dedication marking 'Moscow Collective Farm' on the turret in black or dark green.

BT-7 knocked out in 1941 with a hold-over pre-war turret air band. This style started at the top third of the turret side and overlapped the turret roof by about 33 cm (National Archives).

IS-2 of the 4th Guards Tank Army, Berlin, 1945, showing the unit's insignia (white bear on a red star), a portion of the slogan 'Friend in battle' and the post-April 22 air identification bands.

The specific symbol is closely related to the German divisional symbol. These markings first came into use in 1942 but were not common until 1944-45. Only a handful have been deciphered.

Air identification markings

The Soviet Army made use of air identification bands, painted on turret roofs, in an erratic fashion through the war. At the war's outset, a number of BT-7s and BA-10s used white turret roof crosses, but these soon disappeared. They were uncommon until 1943 when they again saw limited use on a local level in various shapes. The only organised use began on April 21 1945 when all Soviet armoured vehicles in forward combat areas were supposed to have a large roof cross and a wide turret band painted in white added to the vehicles' existing markings. This was caused by requests by the RAF and USAAF in hopes of preventing accidental strafing of Allied vehicles as had occurred in Yugoslavia. Though the use of these bands was not total, they were very common during the Berlin operation. This system was supposed to be replaced in May by one consisting of large white triangles, due to the fact that German tanks had begun to sport these bands as well. However, the war ended before the order had any effect.

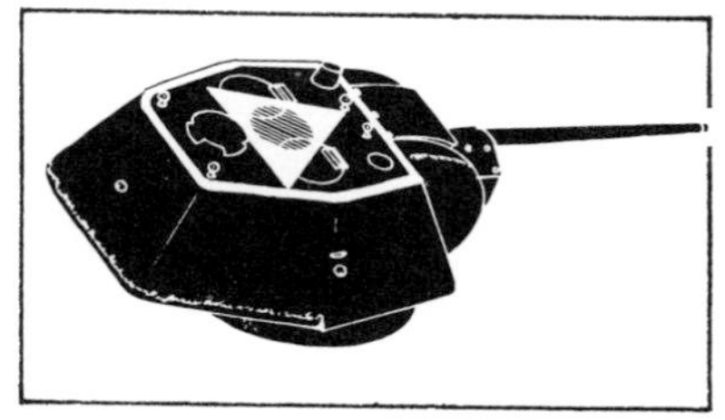

T-34, circa 1943, showing air identification markings which consist of a white triangle with yellow circle and white edging around the roof edge.

In conclusion, it should be noted that the description of Soviet markings given here is a very general one, and there were undoubtedly many exceptions to the rules. Furthermore, there has been so little investigation into this broad area, as compared to say, German markings, that there will undoubtedly be surprises in store for future researchers.

four

Soviet tank data

Data is given in the following pages for all known production tanks used by the Soviet Army from 1939-45—discounting a few hybrid vehicles such as armoured tractors, etc. This excludes armoured cars and self-propelled weapons.

Due to the large number of vehicles involved, no data is given for vehicles from earlier periods that did not participate in World War 2. Neither is it given for experimental models or unarmoured vehicles (ie the lorry-mounted rocket launchers). For the same reason, lengthy text descriptions are also impracticable; it is hoped that the short descriptions given in the preceding pages will suffice.

In some cases data may vary; ie all T-34, KV and IS based SPs may have been produced on several marks, and sometimes may have slight changes resulting from the addition or removal of equipment (eg the use of extra-wide snow tracks, etc).

As regards accuracy of the information, the author has relied upon official Soviet documentation, coupled with various intelligence reports on captured vehicles. One often finds discrepancies of a minor nature between sources, but generally the information tends to correlate satisfactorily.

Left *First of the true Soviet tank destroyers, the SU-85. An SP 85 mm anti-tank gun based on the T-34 tank chassis.* **Below** *The ISU-122 self-propelled 122 mm anti-tank gun based on the Stalin tank chassis.*

Medium Tanks

Vehicle:	BT-2	BT-3	BT-5	BT-5A	BT-7-1	BT-7-2	BT-7A
Weight, in action:	10.2 tons	10.2 tons	11.5 tons	11.7 tons	13.8 tons	13.8 tons	14.2 tons
Max road speed:	69 mph	69 mph	69 mph	69 mph	46 mph	46 mph	42 mph
Road range:	187 miles	187 miles	187 miles	187 miles	310 miles	310 miles	310 miles
Cross-country range:	125 miles	125 miles	125 miles	125 miles	220 miles	220 miles	220 miles
Length overall:	18.0 ft	18.0 ft	18.1 ft	18.0 ft	18.65 ft	18.65 ft	18.0 ft
Width:	7.33 ft	7.33 ft	7.33 ft	7.33 ft	7.98 ft	7.98 ft	7.98 ft
Height:	7.25 ft	7.25 ft	7.25 ft	7.25 ft	7.50 ft	7.50 ft	7.50 ft
Engine:	Liberty Aero 12 Cyl petrol 343 HP	Liberty Aero 12 Cyl petrol 343 HP	M-5 Aero 12 Cyl petrol 350 HP	M-5 Aero 12 Cyl petrol 350 HP	M-17T Liberty 12 Cyl petrol 450 HP	M-17T Liberty 12 Cyl petrol 450 HP	M-17T Liberty 12 Cyl petrol 450 HP
Track width:	10.25 ins	10.25 ins	10.25 ins	10.25 ins	10.25 ins	10.25 ins	10.25 ins
Ground contact:	10.66 ft	12.0 ft	12.0 ft	12.0 ft	12.0 ft	12.0 ft	12.50 ft
Armament:	Two 7.62 mm MGs or 37 mm M1930	45 mm L/46 A/TK gun & 7.62 mm DTMG	45 mm L/46 A/TK gun & 7.62 mm DTMG	76.2 mm L/16.5 gun & 7.62 mm DTMG	45 mm L/46 A/TK gun & two 7.62 mm MGs	45 mm L/46 A/TK gun & two 7.62 mm MGs	76.2 mm L/16.5 gun & two 7.62 mm MGs
Ammunition:	4000 MG or 96 rounds & 2709 MG	96 rounds 2709 MG	72-115 rounds 2394 MG	72-115 rounds 2394 MG	172-188 rounds 2394 MG	132-146 rounds 2394 MG	172-188 rounds 2394 MG
Bow armour:	13 mm	13 mm	13 mm	13 mm	22 mm	22 mm	22 mm
Side armour:	10-13 mm	10-13 mm	10-13 mm	10-13 mm	13 mm	13 mm	13 mm
Roof & floor armour:	6-10 mm	6-10 mm	6-10 mm	6-10 mm	6-10 mm	6-10 mm	6-10 mm
Turret armour:	6-10 mm	10-13 mm	10-13 mm	10-13 mm	10-13 mm	10-13 mm	10-13 mm
Crew:	3 men	3 men	3 men	3 men	3 men	3 men	3 men
Special features:	Early model of BT tank; all service vehicles armed with 37 mm gun and one MG. (BT-1 purely experimental).	Up-gunned version of BT-2; not many produced due to introduction of BT-5 (BT-4 purely experimental).	Improved BT-3 with larger turret. Radio version designated BT-5U (or TU). Bridge-layer version BT-IT. Flame-thrower version BT-50T.	Artillery version of BT-5 mounting short 76.2 mm howitzer in main turret of T-28 tank (modified).	BT-5 with new conical turret, new engine and thicker armour. Radio version designated BT-7U (or BT-7 TU).	BT-7-1 with re-designed hull armour. All vehicles fitted with radio.	Artillery version of BT-7 mounting short 76.2 mm howitzer in main turret of T-28 tank modified).

Medium Tanks (continued)

Vehicle:	BT-7 m	T-28	T-28V	T-28M-1	T-28M-2	T-34/76A	T-34/76B
Weight, in action:	14.65 tons	28.5 tons	31.0 tons	31.0 tons	32.0 tons	26.3 tons	28.0 tons
Max road speed:	54 mph	23 mph	23 mph	14.4 mph	14.4 mph	31.0 mph	31.0 mph
Road range:	440 miles	137 miles	112 miles	110 miles	110 miles	118-280 miles	188-280 miles
Cross-country range:	375 miles	100 miles	90 miles	85 miles	85 miles	130-240 miles	130-240 miles
Length overall:	18.65 ft	24.25 ft	23.62 ft	24.45 ft	24.45 ft	20-22 ft	22 ft
Width:	7.98 ft	9.20 ft	9.20 ft	9.20 ft	9.20 ft	9.8 ft	9.8 ft
Height:	7.50 ft	9.25 ft	9.00 ft	9.25 ft	9.25 ft	8.0 ft	8.0 ft
Engine:	V-2 12 Cyl diesel 500 HP	M-17L Liberty 12 Cyl petrol 500 HP	M-17L Liberty 12 Cyl petrol 500 HP	M-17L Liberty 12 Cyl petrol 500 HP	M-17L Liberty 12 Cyl petrol 500 HP	V-2-34 12 Cyl diesel 500 HP	V-2-34 12 Cyl diesel 500 HP
Track width:	10.25 ins	14.0 ins	14.0 ins	14.0 ins	14.0 ins	19.1 ins	19.1 ins
Ground contact:	12.0 ft	19.18 ft	21.25 ft	21.25 ft	21.25 ft	12.2 ft	12.2 ft
Armament:	76.2 mm L/26 gun two 7.62 mm MGs	76.2 mm L/16.5 gun & other weapons	76.2 mm L/16.5 gun & other weapons	76.2 mm L/26 gun three 7.62 mm DTMGs	76.2 mm L/26 gun three 7.62 mm DTMGs	76.2 mm L/30.5 gun, 2 × 7.62 mm MGs	76.2 mm L/41.2 gun, 2 × 7.62 mm MGs
Ammunition:	40 rounds 2394 MG	70 rounds 7938 MG	70 rounds 7938 MG	70 rounds 7938 MG	70 rounds 7938 MG	80 rounds 2394 MG	77 rounds 2394 MG
Bow armour:	22 mm	30 mm	30 mm	35 mm	50-80 mm	45 mm	60 mm
Side armour:	13 mm	20 mm	20 mm	20 mm	20 mm	40-45 mm	40-45 mm
Roof & floor armour:	6-10 mm	10-15 mm	10-15 mm	10-15 mm	23 mm	15-22 mm	18-22 mm
Turret armour:	10-15 mm	11-20 mm	11-40 mm	11-40 mm	20-80 mm	16-45 mm	16-70 mm
Crew:	3 men	6 men	6 men	6 men	6 men	4 men	4 men
Special features:	Also known as BT-8. BT-7 tank powered by new diesel engine.	First production model of multi-turreted medium tank. Bridge-layer version IT-28, flame-thrower version OT-28.	Also known as T-28A. Modified version of T-28.	Also known as T-28B. Final production model of T-28 tank.	Also known as T-28C. T-28M-1 tank with armoured screens. Modified during Russo-Finnish War 1939/40.	Officially designated T-34 06. 40. First production model of T-34 tank. Some retrofitted with 76.2 mm L/41.2 gun.	Officially designated T-34 06. 41. Up-gunned version of T-34/76A. Various factory variations. A few armed with 57 mm 215.4 gun. Flame-thrower version ATO-41.

Medium Tanks (continued)

Vehicle:	T-34/76C	T-34/76D, E, F	T-43	T-34/85	T-44/85
Weight, in action:	30.2 tons	30.9 tons	31 tons	31.5 tons	31.9 tons
Max road speed:	30 mph	31 mph	31 mph	31 mph	32 mph
Road range:	170-260 miles	180-270 miles	186-220 miles	186-220 miles	145-189 miles
Cross-country range:	120-220 miles	125-230 miles	130-210 miles	130-210 miles	122-155 miles
Length overall:	24.65 ft	21.6 ft	22.5 ft	24.6 ft	25.1 ft
Width:	9.80 ft	9.80 ft	9.8 ft	9.8 ft	10.2 ft
Height:	8.00 ft	8.00-8.45 ft	8.5 ft	7.8 ft	7.85 ft
Engine:	V-2-34 12 Cyl diesel 500 HP	V-2-34 12 Cyl diesel 500 HP	V-2-34 12 Cyl diesel 500 HP	V-2-34 12 Cyl diesel 500 HP	V-2-44 12 Cyl diesel 512 HP
Track width:	19.1 ins	19.1 ins	19.1 ins	19.1 ins	19.8 ins
Ground contact:	12.2 ft	12.2 ft	12.25 ft	12.2 ft	12.65 ft
Armament:	76.2 mm L/41.2 gun one 7.62 mm MG	76.2 mm L/41.2 gun two 7.62 mm MGs	76.2 mm L/41.2 gun two 7.62 mm MGs	85 mm 215-553 L/51.5, 2 MGs	85 mm 215-553 L/51.5, 3 MGs
Ammunition:	45 rounds 2394 MG	77 rounds 2394 MG	77 rounds 2394 MG	55 rounds 2394 MG	58 rounds 1890 MG
Bow armour:	60 mm	45-47 mm	70-110 mm	47-60 mm	70-90 mm
Side armour:	40-45 mm	45 mm	45-47 mm	45-47 mm	75 mm
Roof & floor armour:	18-22 mm	18-22 mm	18-22 mm	18-22 mm	15-20 mm
Turret armour:	20-70 mm	20-70 mm	20-70 mm	20-75 mm	25-120 mm
Crew:	4 men	4 men	4 men	5 men	4 men
Special features:	Officially designated T-34 06. 42. Improved armour layout and other internal sophistications.	Officially designated T-34 06. 42/43. Models D, E, F visually different turret details but not distinguished by Soviets.	Up-armoured version of T-34/76 06. 42/43.	Variations in turret details. Up-gunned T-34/76 06. 42/43 with 85 mm gun.	An unsuccessful successor to T-34/85. Saw limited action. 100 mm gun version being tested at end of war.

Heavy Tanks

Vehicle:	T-32	T-35-1	T-35-2	KV-1	KV-1A	KV-1B	KV-1C
Weight, in action:	44.8 tons	45 tons	46 tons	46.35 tons	43.5 tons	47.5 tons	49.0 tons
Max road speed:	18 mph	18 mph	19 mph	22 mph	22 mph	22 mph	18.4 mph
Road range:	94 miles	94 miles	94 miles	140 miles	140 miles	140 miles	156 miles
Cross-country range:	50 miles	50 miles	50 miles	94 miles	94 miles	94 miles	110 miles
Length overall:	30.5 ft	31.5 ft	31.9 ft	22.6 ft	22.3 ft	22.3 ft	22.3 ft
Width:	10.5 ft	10.5 ft	10.5 ft	10.65 ft	10.93 ft	10.93 ft	10.93 ft
Height:	10.0 ft	11.25 ft	10.5 ft	8.75 ft	8.88 ft	10.65 ft	10.65 ft
Engine:	M-17L 12 Cyl petrol 345 HP	M-17M 12 Cyl petrol 500 HP	M-17M 12 Cyl petrol 500 HP	V-2K 12 Cyl diesel 550 HP	V-2K 12 Cyl diesel 550 HP	V-2K 12 Cyl diesel 550 HP	V-2K 12 Cyl diesel 550 HP
Track width:	12.18 ins	12.18 ins	12.18 ins	27.5 ins	27.5 ins	27.5 ins	27.5 ins
Ground contact:	26.1 ft	26.1 ft	26.1 ft	14.2 ft	13.8 ft	13.8 ft	13.8 ft
Armament:	Main-76.2 mm L/16.5 & others	Main 76.2 mm L/16.5 & others	Main 76.2 mm L/24 & others	76.2 mm M1938/39 L/30.5, 3 MGs	76.2 mm M1940 L/41.5, 3 MGs	76.2 mm M1938/39 L/30.5, 3 MGs	76.2 mm M1940 L/41.5, 3 MGs
Ammunition:	96 (main)	96 (main)	96 (main)	111 rounds 3024 MG	111 rounds 3024 MG	111 rounds 3024 MG	114 rounds 3024 MG
Bow armour:	25 mm	30 mm	35 mm	106 mm	110 mm	110 mm	110 mm
Side armour:	20 mm	20 mm	25 mm	75-77 mm	75-77 mm	75-110 mm	90-110 mm
Roof & floor armour:	11-14 mm	11-14 mm	11-14 mm	30-40 mm	35 mm	35 mm	35-40 mm
Turret armour:	11-20 mm	11-20 mm	11-35 mm	30-100 mm	35-110 mm	35-100 mm	40-120 mm
Crew:	10 men	10 men	7 men	5 men	5 men	5 men	5 men
Special features:	First production heavy tank. 3 turrets, 6 wheels per side.	Improved T-32 3 turrets, 8 wheels per side.	Improved T-35-1 less turrets, 8 wheels per side.	First single-turreted heavy tank. Powerfully built, well-armed and good perofrmance. Torsion bar suspension.	The letter suffixes are of Western origin. No Soviet system exists to clearly distinguish between models.	Cast and bolted turret variants were produced. Flame-thrower version designated KV-8, had 45 mm gun & flame-thrower in turret.	Up-armoured KV-1B.

Heavy Tanks (continued)

Vehicle:	KV-1s	KV-85	KV-2A	KV-2B	IS-1(85)	IS-1(122)	IS-2(122)
Weight, in action:	42.5 tons	46 tons	53 tons	57 tons	44 tons	44.5 tons	45.0 tons
Max road speed:	25 mph	22 mph	16 mph	16 mph	23 mph	23 mph	23 mph
Road range:	156 miles	156 miles	100 miles	100 miles	150 miles	150 miles	150 miles
Cross-country range:	110 miles	93 miles	84 miles	84 miles	130 miles	130 miles	130 miles
Length overall:	22.1 ft	27.85 ft	22.3 ft	22.3 ft	27.3 ft	31.5 ft	31.5 ft
Width:	10.7 ft	10.66 ft	10.93 ft	10.93 ft	10.25 ft	10.25 ft	10.25 ft
Height:	9.8 ft	9.5 ft	12.0 ft	13.7 ft	8.9 ft	8.9 ft	8.9 ft
Engine:	V-2K-s 12 Cyl diesel 600 HP	V-2K-s 12 Cyl diesel 600 HP	V-2K 12 Cyl diesel 550 HP	V-2K 12 Cyl diesel 550 HP	V-2-IS (V2K) 12 Cyl diesel 513 HP	V-2-IS (V2K) 12 Cyl diesel 513 HP	V-2-IS (V2K) 12 Cyl diesel 513 HP
Track width:	28.0 ins	28.0 ins	27.5 ins	27.5 ins	25.63 ins	25.63 ins	25.63 ins
Ground contact:	13.8 ft	14.4 ft	14.4 ft	14.4 ft	14.3 ft	14.3 ft	14.3 ft
Armament:	7.62 mm M1940 L/41.5, 3 MGs	85 mm M1943 L/51.5, 3 MGs	152 mm M1938/40 how, 2 × 7.62 mm MG	152 mm M1938/40 how, 2 × 7.62 mm MG	85 mm M1943 gun 3 × 7.62 mm MG	122 mm M1943 3 × 7.62 mm MG	122 mm M1943 3 × 7.62 mm MG
Ammunition:	102 rounds 3042 MG	71 rounds 3276 MG	36 rounds 3087 MG	36 rounds 3087 MG	71 rounds 1330 MG	28 rounds 2330 MG	28 rounds 2330 MG
Bow armour:	75 mm	60-75 mm	110 mm	110 mm	120 mm	120 mm	120 mm
Side armour:	60 mm	60-65 mm	75-77 mm	75-110 mm	89-90 mm	89-90 mm	89-90 mm
Roof & floor armour:	35 mm	30 mm	35 mm	35 mm	25 mm	25 mm	25 mm
Turret armour:	30-82 mm	30-110 mm	35-100 mm	35-100 mm	30-100 mm	30-102 mm	30-102 mm
Crew:	5 men	4 men	6 men	6 men	4 men	4 men	4 men
Special features:	lightened, faster version of KV-1.	Up-gunned version of KV-1s.	Close-support version of KV-1 mounting short 152 mm howitzer. Not very successful.	Improved KV-2A.	Original Stalin heavy tank armed with 85 mm gun. Sometimes mounted 12.7 mm DShK AAMG.	Up-gunned IS-1(85) with 122 mm tank gun. Can mount DShK AAMG.	IS-1 with re-designed armour layout, 122 mm tank gun and can mount DShK AAMG.

Light Tanks

Vehicle:	T-27A	T-27B	T-37	T-37A	T-38	T-38M2	T-26A
Weight, in action:	1.9 tons	2.68 tons	3.5 tons	3.9 tons	3.28 tons	3.8 tons	7-8.5 tons
Max road speed:	25 mph	25 mph	40 mph	40 mph	28 mph	40 mph	22 mph
Road range:	53 miles	100 miles	143 miles	115 miles	156 miles	160 miles	87 miles
Cross-country range:	38 miles	38 miles	64 miles	60 miles	137 miles	140 miles	60 miles
Length overall:	8.1 ft	8.5 ft	12.26 ft	12.26 ft	12.35 ft	12.35 ft	15.76 ft
Width:	6.0 ft	5.5 ft	6.51 ft	6.51 ft	7.65 ft	7.65 ft	7.85 ft
Height:	4.5 ft	4.76 ft	5.91 ft	5.91 ft	5.33 ft	5.15 ft	6.75 ft
Engine:	GAZ AA 4 Cyl Petrol 40 HP	GAZ AA 4 Cyl Petrol 40 HP	GAZ AA 4 Cyl Petrol 65 HP	GAZ AA 4 Cyl Petrol 65 HP	GAZ AA 4 Cyl Petrol 40 HP	GAZ MI 4 Cyl Petrol 50 HP	GAZ T-26 8 Cyl Petrol 88-91 HP
Track width:	5.5 ins	5.5 ins	8.26 ins	8.26 ins	7.5 ins	7.5 ins	10.2 ins
Ground contact:	4.5 ft	4.76 ft	5.91 ft	5.91 ft	5.33 ft	5.15 ft	9.75 ft
Armament:	One 7.62 mm DT MG	One 7.62 mm DT MG	One 7.62 mm DT or 12.7 mm DShK	One 7.62 mm DT or 12.7 mm DShK	One 7.62 mm DT MG	One 7.62 mm DT MG	Numerous (see text)
Ammunition:	2520 rounds	2520 rounds	585 rounds	585 rounds	1512 rounds	1512 rounds	Depending on arament
Bow armour:	10 mm	10 mm	9.5 mm	10 mm	9.5 mm	9.5 mm	15 mm
Side armour:	9-10 mm	9-10 mm	7 mm	10 mm	9 mm	9 mm	15 mm
Roof & floor armour:	4-6 mm	4-6 mm	4 mm	5-7 mm	4 mm	4 mm	6-10 mm
Turret armour:	No turret	No turret	4-6 mm	4-6 mm	4-6 mm	4-6 mm	6-15 mm
Crew:	2 men	2 men	2 men	2 men	2 men	2 men	3 men
Special features:	Developed from English Carden-Loyd Mk VI machine-gun carrier. Prototype 1931. 348 T-27As produced. 2500 T-27Bs produced. Various experimental SPs based on these chassis. When obsolete majority of vehicles converted to driver-training vehicles or artillery/ammunition tractors.		Developed from English Carden-Loyd. Amphibious Tank (A4E11). Various prototype amphibious tanks 1931-2 (T-33, T-41). Third prototype, T-37 accepted 1933. Commander's models T-37U and T-37 TU. Various hybrid conversions. 1200 built.		Prototype built at Factory No. 37 in Moscow 1935. Modified version T-38M2 with more powerful engine and new transmission. Special variants with 20 mm cannon in turret or hull. Radio-Controlled version. Production ceased 1939. 1940 — TM experimental model with lengthened chassis.		8 Vickers 6-ton tanks purchased 1930. TMM series prototypes 1931. 1932 production began 12,000 produced by 1940. Numerous variants incl. T-26 TU Command and OT-26 flame-tank.

Light Tanks (continued)

Vehicle:	T-26B	T-26S	T-46	T-40	T-40A	T-40S	T-50
Weight, in action:	9.2-9.6 tons	10.3 tons	10.2 tons	5.5 tons	6.2 tons	6.1 tons	13.5 tons
Max road speed:	18 mph	17 mph	35-36 mph	28 mph	26 mph	26 mph	33 mph
Road range:	140 miles	215 miles	224-310 miles	222 miles	210 miles	216 miles	220 miles
Cross-country range:	110 miles	109 miles	180-250 miles	115 miles	100 miles	110 miles	172 miles
Length overall:	15.76 ft	15.25 ft	18.0 ft	13.5 ft	14.0 ft	13.9 ft	17.0 ft
Width:	7.85 ft	8.0 ft	7.66 ft	7.65 ft	7.65 ft	7.65 ft	8.1 ft
Height:	7.95 ft	7.65 ft	7.5 ft	6.48 ft	6.48 ft	6.38 ft	7.1 ft
Engine:	GAZ T-26 8 Cyl petrol 88-91 HP	GAZ T-26 8 Cyl petrol 88-91 HP	GAZ T-26 8 Cyl petrol 88-91 HP	GAZ-202 6 Cyl petrol 85 HP	GAZ-202 6 Cyl petrol 85 HP	GAZ-202 6 Cyl petrol 85 HP	GAZ V-4 6 Cyl diesel 300 HP
Track width:	10.2 ins	10.2 ins	10.25 ins	7.0 ins	7.0 ins	7.0 ins	17.0 ins
Ground contact:	9.75 ft	9.75 ft	12.0 ft	7.66 ins	7.66 ins	7.66 ins	9.5 ins
Armament:	37 mm or 45 mm A/TK gun & MG	45 mm L/46 A/TK gun & 2 × MGs	45 mm L/46 A/TK gun & MG	12.7 mm DShK or 20 mm & MG	12.7 mm DShK or 20 mm & MG	12.7 mm DShK or 20 mm & MG	45 mm L/46 A/TK gun & MG
Ammunition:	92-100 rounds 3000 MG	165 rounds 3654 MG	165 rounds 3654 MG	550 rounds 2016 MG	550 rounds 2016 MG	550 rounds 2016 MG	150 rounds 4000 MG
Bow armour:	15 mm	25 mm	15 mm	13 mm	14 mm	14 mm	37 mm
Side armour:	15 mm	16 mm	15 mm	13 mm	14 mm	14 mm	37 mm
Roof & floor armour:	6-10 mm	10 mm	6-10 mm	6-10 mm	6-10 mm	10 mm	12-15 mm
Turret armour:	6-15 mm	10-25 mm	6-15 mm	7-14 mm	7-14 mm	7-14 mm	15-37 mm
Crew:	3 men	3 men	3 men	2 men	2 men	2 men	4 men
Special features:	Single-turreted version of T-26A. Several specialised vehicles used this chassis, e.g. AT-26 SP, OT-130 and PT-133 FT tanks, IT-26 bridgelayer, etc.	Improved T-26B with thicker, welded armour now inclined. OT-133 flame-throwing variant existed.	Wheel/track version of T-26 with Christie suspension — limited production only.	Light amphibious tank as a replacement for T-38. Torsion bar suspension.	Up-armoured version of T-40.	Up-armoured version of T-40, no longer amphibious.	Diesel-engined light tank with equal armour all around. Called 'Maliy Klim' by troops.

Light Tanks (continued)

Vehicle:	T-60	T-60A	T-70	T-70A	T-80
Weight, in action:	5.75 tons	6.4 tons	9.05 tons	10.0 tons	11.6 tons
Max road speed:	28 mph	26 mph	32 mph	28 mph	25 mph
Road range:	384 miles	375 miles	279 miles	260 miles	200 miles
Cross-country range:	197 miles	188 miles	186 miles	175 miles	145 miles
Length overall:	13.1 ft	13.65 ft	15.28 ft	15.48 ft	15.49 ft
Width:	7.5 ft	7.66 ft	7.68 ft	8.1 ft	8.47 ft
Height:	5.75 ft	5.85 ft	6.78 ft	6.66 ft	7.15 ft
Engine:	GAZ-202 6 Cyl petrol 70 HP	GAZ-202 6 Cyl petrol 85 HP	2 × 215-202 6 Cyl, 2 × 70 HP	2 × GAZ-203 6 Cyl, 2 × 85 HP	2 × GAZ-203 6 Cyl, 2 × 85 HP
Track width:	7.0 ins	7.0 ins	17.5 ins	17.5 ins	17.5 ins
Ground contact:	7.5 ft	7.5 ft	10.25 ft	10.25 ft	10.25 ft
Armament:	20 mm ShVAK Cannon & MG	20 mm ShVAK Cannon & MG	45 mm L/46 A/TK gun & MG	45 mm L/46 A/TK gun & MG	45 mm L/46 A/TK gun & MG
Ammunition:	780 rounds 945 MG	780 rounds 945 MG	66-70 rounds 945 MG	94 rounds 1008 MG	94 rounds 1008 MG
Bow armour:	14.20 mm	35 mm	35-40 mm	35-45 mm	50 mm
Side armour:	15 mm	25 mm	16 mm	16 mm	16-25 mm
Roof & floor armour:	7-10 mm	13 mm	10 mm	10 mm	15 mm
Turret armour:	7-15 mm	25 mm	10-60 mm	10-70 mm	20-70 mm
Crew:	2 men	2 men	2 men	2 men	3 men
Special features:	Purely land-based light tank intended for reconnaissance units.	Up-armoured version of T-60.	Re-design of T-60 with twin engines and better armour layout.	Up-armoured version of T-70.	Final production light tank of World War 2. Up-armoured, extra crew member.